QUESTIONS & ANSWERS

Painting and Decorating

Padim Technical Authors

Alfred Fulcher

Brian Rhodes

Bill Stewart

Derick Tickle

John Windsor

Newnes Technical Books

£4·00

The Butterworth Group

United Kingdom   **Butterworth & Co (Publishers) Ltd**
        London: 88 Kingsway, WC2B 6AB

Australia   **Butterworths Pty Ltd**
        Sydney: 586 Pacific Highway, NSW 2067
        Also at Melbourne, Brisbane, Adelaide and Perth

Canada   **Butterworth & Co (Canada) Ltd**
        Toronto: 2265 Midland Avenue, Scarborough,
          Ontario, M1P 4S1

New Zealand   **Butterworths of New Zealand Ltd**
        Wellington: T & W Young Building,
          77–85 Customhouse Quay, 1 CPO Box 472

South Africa   **Butterworth & Co (South Africa) (Pty) Ltd**
        Durban: 152–154 Gale Street

USA   **Butterworth (Publishers) Inc**
        Boston: 19 Cummings Park, Woburn, Mass. 01801

First published 1978 by Newnes Technical Books
a Butterworth imprint

© Butterworth & Co (Publishers) Ltd, 1978

Illustrations © Padim Technical Authors 1978

British Library Cataloguing in Publication Data

Padim Technical Authors
   Painting and decorating. — (Questions and answers
series).
   1.   House painting   2.   Painting, Industrial   3.   Interior
decoration
   I.   Title   II.   Series
   698   TH8203

ISBN 0-408-00321-9

Typeset by Butterworth Litho-Preparation Department

Printed in England by Cox & Wyman Ltd.,
London, Fakenham and Reading

PREFACE

A definitive book on painting and decorating cannot be contained within a volume of this size. It has therefore been decided to include only those materials, processes and elements of job knowledge that would probably be required when decorating a house.

Although some painting contractors and small decorators may disagree with our reasons, this limited field means that no aspect of spray painting has been included. The small range of mechanical tools now commonly used by the painter has been given adequate coverage but the more specialised equipment, particularly that used for steel preparations, has been omitted. The emphasis has been placed principally on how a job is done with only a brief description of the 'whys' associated with the answer. Questions have been posed on safe working and safety equipment in an effort to make persons involved in painting work more aware of the increasing number of hazards in this respect.

Because of its involvement with the basic work of the painter and decorator, the book will be of value to the new entrant to the painting industry. Although it does not pretend to fully cover the scope of the City and Guilds of London Institutes Craft syllabus it will be an important reference book for the craft level student. The DIY painter and decorator will find the answer to many specific queries together with sufficient knowledge for individual jobs. This can be applied to the other problems for which we have not designed a specific question.

The book has been written by a group of lecturers in painting and decorating with a wealth of practical and teaching experience. This combined academic and practical approach has produced a text valuable to any student of building or any practitioner of building whose experience involves the finishing of buildings.

CONTENTS

1

TOOLS AND EQUIPMENT

What tools are essential for preparing surfaces?

Stripping knife or scraper; filling knife; stopping or putty knife; shavehook; wire brush. These tools are illustrated in Figs 1–5 and their properties and uses are listed in the Table on page 2.

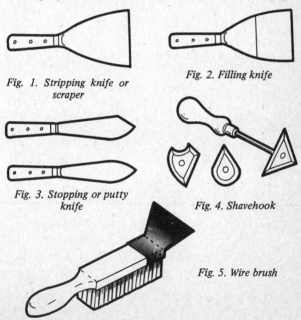

Fig. 1. Stripping knife or scraper

Fig. 2. Filling knife

Fig. 3. Stopping or putty knife

Fig. 4. Shavehook

Fig. 5. Wire brush

Tool	Sizes	Properties	Uses
Stripping knife or scraper (Fig. 1)	15 – 100 mm wide	Rigid blades capable of retaining a good edge	Removing old wallpaper, old paint films and loosely attached deposits from flat surfaces
Filling knife (Fig. 2)	25 – 100 mm wide	Similar to stripping knife in appearance but the blade is very flexible	Applying paste fillers to uneven surfaces and to fill grain in timber
Stopping or putty knife (Fig. 3)	Only one size available	Rigid blade, available in two shapes	Forcing putty stoppers into holes and cracks. Finishing putties when glazing
Shavehook (Fig. 4)	One size only available in three shapes; some fixed, others with interchangeable heads.	Has a bevelled cutting edge round the blade which must be kept sharp using a a file	Removing paint and debris from mouldings and beads usually in conjunction with paint remover and when burning off. Raking out cracks in plaster before filling
Wire brush (Fig. 5)	Sizes vary but usually about 300 mm long	Wire filaments set into a wooden handle	Removing old loose, flaking or powdery paint films, rust and other debris from iron; concrete, brick and renderings

What qualities should be looked for when purchasing tools?

1. The shaft or blade should be one piece and extend through to the end of the handle (Fig. 6a)
2. The steel should be flexible (Fig. 6b)

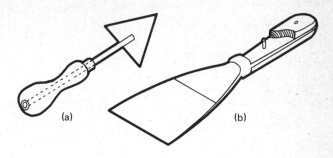

Fig. 6. Steel tools

Why do paint brushes vary in price?

There are several reasons. The price has a direct relationship with what is known as the 'Filling' (Fig. 7)
1. The main types of filling used, are:
 (i) *Pure bristle* – most expensive.

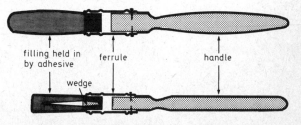

Fig. 7. Paint brush components

(ii)   *Man made filaments* – cheaper than bristle.
(iii) *Various types of hair* – cheapest.

2. Good brushes are carefully shaped towards a taper or wedge shape and have good length out.

3. Some brushes are very full, others have large filling strips or packing wedges inside the ferrule. This reduces the amount of filling used and cheapens the brush. Less filling holds less paint.

What are the uses for the various sizes of paint brush?

Size	Uses
25 mm and 38 mm	(i) Cutting in window, panels, skirting, and angles.
	(ii) Painting pipes, railings and ornamental iron work.
50 mm	Application of most types of paint, to door panels small areas such as reveals, skirtings and cupboards.
75 mm	Application of undercoat and gloss finishes to larger areas such as flush doors and wall surfaces.
100 mm	Application of undercoat, eggshell, gloss and emulsion paints to walls and ceilings.
150 mm 175 mm 180 mm 200 mm	(i) Application of emulsion paint to walls and ceilings. (ii) Application of paste to wallpapers.

How would one select a brush for a specific job?

It is best to choose the largest brush possible for a particular job. For example, it is quicker and easier to apply gloss paint to a flush door with a 75 mm brush than with a 50 mm brush.

   Also, the length of filling should be considered:

   (i) Long fillings hold more paint, a useful property when applying undercoats and emulsion paints.

4

(ii) Shorter, slightly worn fillings are better for the application of gloss paints.

What are the qualities of brush fillings?

Pure Bristle is the best type of filling because of the following properties:

    Resilience or flexibility. This enables the filling to spring back into place as it is used.

    Flag. The thin end of each bristle which splits into several fine pieces, providing a soft tip for laying-off (Fig. 8).

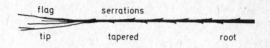

Fig. 8. Various parts of a bristle

    Serrations. These are like small scales along the length which help to hold the paint.

    Taper. A natural taper from the thin tip or flag to the thicker root, this allows the brush to form a tapered wedge shape.

Hair. These are cheap fillings which have no flag, serrations or taper and are less resilient than bristle.

Man-made fibre fillings, including Nylon, Perlon, Tynex, and Orel, have been produced to take the place of bristle which is becoming increasingly scarce. These fillings are very springy, tough, more hard wearing than bristle. They can be tapered and flagged mechanically but they do not hold paint as well as bristle.

Fibre fillings have no flag or taper, are coarse and have very poor resilience. Fibre is sometimes mixed with bristle and hair for the cheaper brushes and used alone for washing-down brushes.

What is the minimum paperhanging tool kit?

A basic selection of tools is given in the following table. It is also useful to have a paperhanger's apron with kangaroo pocket to hold the tools while working.

Tool	Sizes	Uses
Paperhanging brush (Fig. 9)	200 mm 225 mm 250 mm	Smooths the paper and presses it against the surface
Scissors or shears (Fig. 10)	250 mm 275 mm 300 mm	(i) Cut lengths (ii) Trim angles and around obstacles

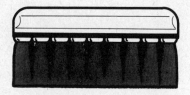

Fig. 9. Paperhanging brush

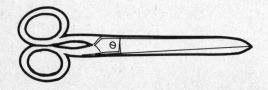

Fig. 10. Scissors for cutting wallpaper

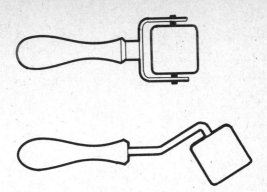

Fig. 11. Seam and angle rollers used for paperhanging

Seam and angle rollers (Fig. 11)	25 mm 37 mm	Roll paper at joints and angles (never used on embossed paper)
Rule (Fig. 12)	1 m long	Measure lengths and widths
Trimming knife (Fig. 13)	One size available with replacement blades	Trim at angles, around obstacles and along lengths

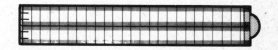

Fig. 12. (above) 1 metre rule
Fig. 13. (left) Trimming knife

Plumb bob and line (Fig. 14)		Check that the paper is upright
Paste brush (Fig. 15)	100 – 175 mm	Application of adhesives

Fig. 14. Plumb bob and line

Fig. 15. Paste brush

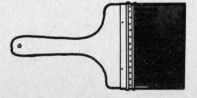

What are the types of paint roller?

There are three basic types of roller:

Cylinder Rollers in widths from 150 mm to 450 mm wide (Fig. 16). The sleeves or covers can be:

(a) *Lambswool.* Available in long, medium and short pile.

(b) *Mohair.* Always a short pile.

(c) *Man-made fibre* (Orel, Nylon, Tynex, Perlon) available in extra long, long, medium and short pile.

(d) *Foamed plastic.*

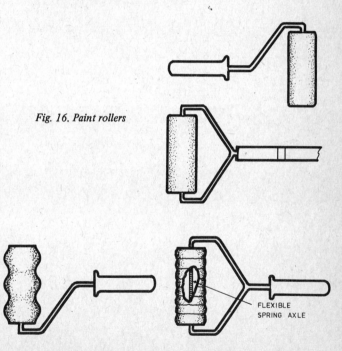

Fig. 16. Paint rollers

FLEXIBLE
SPRING AXLE

Fig. 17. Shaped roller for painting corrugated sheets

Fig. 18. Flexible rollers for painting pipework

Shaped rollers of foamed plastic in various sizes up to 200 mm wide (Fig. 17).
Flexible rollers of lambswool or man-made fibre, in various sizes (Fig. 18) which wrap around pipes.

What are the best uses for these rollers?

Long pile rollers up to 32mm long, can be used for textured surfaces such as brick, concrete and pebbledash.

Medium pile rollers, up to 20mm long, are general purpose tools for smooth, medium and rough surfaces such as embossed papers, concrete and brickwork. They are ideal for water thinned paints.

Short pile rollers, 10mm long and less, are suitable for applying emulsion and oil paints to smooth and low textured surfaces, e.g. emulsion paints to ceilings and walls and gloss paint to walls and flush doors.

Foam rollers are quite cheap and are often thrown away after the job. They tend to skid over the surface and apply the paint unevenly.

Shaped rollers are used for painting large areas of corrugated sheets.

Flexible rollers are necessary for various sizes of pipe. They adjust themselves according to the circumference of the pipe.

What are the types of paint container?

Kettles; paint trays; buckets or scuttles. Available sizes and uses are listed in the table below.

Type	Sizes	Uses
Paint kettle or pot of galvanised iron or plastic (Fig. 19)	Various sizes holding from ¾ – 2½ litres. Also available in diameter sizes	To hold paint decanted from the manufacturers container

Fig. 19. Paint kettle and pot

Fig. 20. Paint tray

Fig. 21. Paint scuttle

Paint trays (Fig. 20)	Various sizes available to take from 150 – 350 mm wide rollers	To hold paint for roller application. Also ensure even take up of paint
Tank, bucket or scuttle (Fig. 21)	Various sizes to take up to 10 litres of paint	To hold larger quantities of paint for roller application. Can be fitted to ladders and steps

How can steel tools be kept in good condition?

1. Ensure they are clean and dry when job is completed.
2. Smear a thin layer of grease over the metal before storing.

Fig. 22. The blade of a steel tool protected with a shield of card or wood

3. Protect the blades with simple card or wool shield (Fig. 22).
4. Keep the edge sharp.

Can paint be left in brushes and rollers for short periods?

Yes; the air must be excluded otherwise the paint will dry in the brush or roller and be difficult to clean out. Three ways of doing this are:
1. Cover the filling or cylinder completely with paint.
2. Place in an air-tight plastic bag with the air pushed out and the top tied.
3. Stand or suspend brushes in water to cover the filling.

How are brushes and rollers cleaned?

1. Remove paint with appropriate solvent e.g. water for emulsions and white spirit or paraffin for oil paints. Only small

12

quantities need to be used at a time changing frequently until all the paint appears to have been removed.

2. Wash thoroughly in warm detergent solution or brush cleaner and finally rinse with clean water.

3. Spin or shake to remove as much of the water as possible.

4. Hang up to dry naturally in a normal temperature 18°C.

(*Note*. Caustic soda will destroy bristle brushes and natural fleeces.)

What precautions must be taken when storing paint brushes and rollers?

1. Never store until they are clean and dry.

2. Never stack, lay or wrap in a manner which can distort and damage the filling or pile.

3. Always suspend rollers.

4. Always store in clean dry and well ventilated conditions.

(*Note*. Mildew and moths may destroy fillings and coverings.)

What personal protective equipment is available and when is it necessary?

Gloves; goggles; masks; and helmets (see table below). Limited protection can be obtained by applying barrier cream to the hands before commencing work.

Gloves	Characteristics
Lightweight (rubber or pvc)	All washing processes when using strong detergent or spirits to protect against dermatitis
Industrial gauntlet type (rubberised fabric)	Using corrosive solutions such as caustic soda

Goggles	
General purpose	Mechanical abrasion of wood, metal or stone Using corrosive solutions particularly when working above head height
Anti-glare	Using flame cleaning equipment

Masks

Dust respirators	Mechanical abrasion of wood, metal stone or asbestos Spray painting
Fume respirators	Applying spirit based paints or spirit paint removers in enclosed areas
Breathing equipment	Working in any unventilated areas
Helmets (hard hats or safety helmets) Fibreglass or plastic	Protect against objects falling, scaffold or building projections

What types of equipment are available for burning off paint?

Blowlamps and torches. The various types and characteristics are given in the following table.

Type	*Characteristics*
Fuel: Paraffin Blowlamp (Fig. 23)	Cheap to operate Fuel readily available Slow lighting procedure No control of flame Heavy Cools quickly in cold weather and winds Requires pumping to maintain pressure.
Fuel: Liquefied Petroleum Gas (LPG) Independent torch (Fig. 24)	Immediate lighting Light to handle Controllable flame Constant pressure Can be used at any angle Can be used with large gas cylinders Gas dearer than paraffin.

14

Bottle-type torch (Fig. 25)	Immediate lighting
	Controllable flame
	Convenient for use on ladders and scaffold
	May not operate when turned on side
	Heavy
	Gas more expensive in small bottles than in larger cylinders.

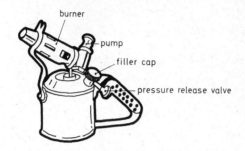

Figure 23. Paraffin blowlamp

Fig. 24. Independent torch using liquid petroleum gas

Fig. 25. Bottle-type torch

15

Fig. 26. Disposable cartridge-type torch

Disposable cartridge type	Immediate lighting
	Controllable flame
	Convenient for use on scaffolds
	Usually cooler flame than other LPG torches
	Some cartridges difficult to handle
	Most expensive form in which to buy LPG
	May not operate when turned on side.

What are the main types of electrical sander?

Disc, belt and orbital sanders. The table below lists their characteristics and uses.

Type	*Characteristics and uses*
Disc Fast spinning disc attached to drill chuck or an adaptation of a grinder. Abrasive discs fitted to rubber pad by central screw or adhesive (Fig. 27)	Very fast action Will remove paint and smooth rough timber Difficult to control and for getting into angles Creates considerable dust Liable to damage surface.

16

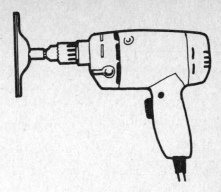

Fig. 27. Disc sander

Orbital
Flat rectangular pad which moves in a small circular motion. Cut sheets of abrasive paper clipped to pad (Fig. 28)

Ideal for final smoothing operation after disc or belt sanding
Easy to control
Can get into angles
Slow abrasive action on rough timber or painted surfaces.

Fig. 28. Orbital sander

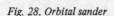

17

Belt

Continuous belt of abrasive paper which is driven around a series of rollers (Fig. 29)

Can be adapted for sanding floors
Faster action than orbital sanders
Often connected to a dust vacuum collector
Expensive and rather cumbersome.

Fig. 29. Belt sander

What is a steam stripper?

An apparatus designed to produce steam that can be directed onto a wall or ceiling to remove:

1. Thick layers of paper;
2. Varnished or painted papers;
3. Thick distemper or other water borne coatings.

A steam stripper leaves the surface clean and sterile. There are two types in common use:

LPG fuelled
(Fig. 30)

Water is placed in the boiler and heated by a gas burner. Steam is generated in 15–20 minutes. Cheap to operate but large and heavy to move around.

Electrically-heated
(Fig. 31)

Water is heated by an electrically heated coil. Steam is generated in 10–15 minutes. More expensive to operate than the LPG type but lighter and more easily moved around.

What are the advantages of a double-insulated tool?

The symbol in Fig. 32 means that the body of the power tool is not connected electrically to the motor. Should the electrical

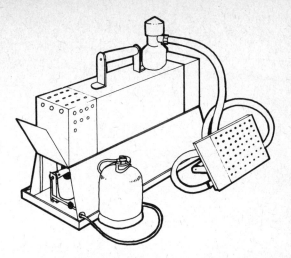

Fig. 30. Steam wallpaper stripper – LPG fuelled

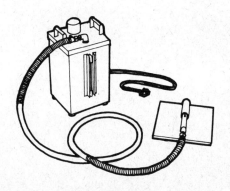

Fig. 31. Steam wallpaper stripper – electrically heated

19

Fig. 32. Symbol for double-insulated appliance

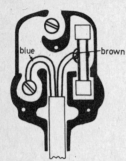

blue · brown

Fig. 33. Flex connections for double-insulated appliance

part of the tool develop a fault the outer casing could not pass on a shock to the user. With this safety device the flex does not require an earth wire.

The flex consists of two cores, the brown one must be attached to the live connector and the blue one to the neutral connector of the plug (see Fig. 33).

2

PREPARATION AND PAINTING
OF SURFACES

Can new plaster be painted?

Yes, if it is dry enough. When the surface is to be coated only
with a water thinned coating such as emulsion paint, or hung
with a non-washable type of wallpaper, it is not essential that
all traces of water should have dried out. If an oil paint system,
such as eggshell or gloss, is to be applied or the surface is to be
hung with a washable or vinyl paper the plaster must be
completely dry.

The time required for a plastered surface to dry completely
varies according to the thickness of the plaster, the type of
plaster used, the time of the year and the temperature of the
room. Outside walls will take longer to dry because the plaster
is often applied to the brickwork (or blocks) and a considerable
thickness (up to 20 mm) may be necessary. Ceilings and
partition walls are commonly covered with plaster board and
thinly coated with plaster and therefore dry faster than the
outside walls. In summer ceiling and partition walls may dry in
a week, whereas outside walls may require 2—3 weeks. In winter
months, particularly if the house is unheated, drying times
may be trebled.

How is plaster prepared to make it ready for painting?

Scrape off any debris with a stripping knife. Lightly dry
abrade with F2 glasspaper to remove plaster splashes and
grit. Remove dust with a dusting brush. Holes and cracks should
be raked out and filled with plaster or filler.

The surface is then ready for sealing with either a thinned emulsion paint if the finish is to be emulsion; a plaster primer, if eggshell or gloss paint is to be used; or a coat of size if it is to be papered. Any efflorescence on the surface should be treated in the manner described in painting outside walls below.

Can outside brick or stone be waterproofed without painting?

A transparent water repellant based on silicone resin is available which seals the pores of the substrate but does not change its colour.

What types of paints are most suitable for brickwork and rendering?

Most manufacturers produce a range of materials called masonry paints for this purpose. With very few exceptions they are water thinned coatings containing fine aggregate such as fine stonedust which gives the film greater thickness, a coarse texture and hard wearing properties. Very absorbent or friable substrates should be sealed with a coating supplied by the manufacturer of the masonry paint. The coatings are available in a range of colours and can be brushed or rolled.

There are also exterior emulsion paints which are cheaper than masonry paints but generally less durable. Oil paint systems can be applied also but they are comparatively expensive.

How are outside walls prepared for painting?

There are four essential areas of attention:
   (a) Ensure that there are no large holes or cracks through which moisture can penetrate. Particular attention should be given to the mortar joints between bricks and stones. If these are powdery, or cracked, they should be raked out and repointed. Large holes should be stopped with a 3:1 sand and cement mixture. This

process is particularly essential if a silicone water repellant is to be applied.

(b) Remove all traces of moss or lichen and wall climbing plants like ivy and virginia creeper by scraping with a stripping knife and wire brushing. Treat the surface with a proprietary solution that will kill all traces of the growths.

(c) Brush thoroughly with a wire or stiff brush to remove all dust, loose particles such as old flaking coatings and traces of efflorescence. This is a white crystalline deposit which may appear on any wet brickwork or plaster. It may reoccur therefore the surface should be left for a few days after brushing to ensure that it is no longer active.

(d) The surface must be dry. If it is particularly wet because of rising damp through either a poor or non-existent damp-proof course, or broken gutters and pipes, or leaking roofs, these must be repaired before any decoration can be effective or durable.

Can asbestos cement sheeting be painted effectively?

Yes. Emulsion paint or water thinned masonry paint can be applied directly to these surfaces providing they are dry and free from dust. If an oil paint system is required an alkali resisting primer is essential as the first coat to prevent the lime in the cement destroying the oil content of the paint.

When used on outside surfaces the edges and back of the sheeting should be coated before fixing with a waterproof coating such as bitumen, if the edges are not visible; or silicone water repellant if they are. Without this precaution the sheeting will absorb moisture which may cause the finish paint to flake or saponify.

What preparation is necessary before painting timber?

Dry abrade the surface with glasspaper or garnet paper fixed to a block or on a finishing sander to remove roughness and flatten the grain. An F2 or equivalent grade paper should be used first followed by a finer paper. If the timber is rubbed in the direction of the grain there is less chance of scratching.

After removing the dust, all nails should be punched below the surface and screws countersunk. The knots in softwood must be coated with shellac knotting to prevent the resins later staining the paint. The knotting should be applied thinly, without misses and to extend beyond the edge of the knot by about 3 mm.

How should building boards be treated before painting?

Most building boards are fixed to timber frames by nails or screws. If these are not galvanised, they may rust if coated with emulsion paint or hung with paper. Therefore, all nail and screw heads must be coated with metal primer first. There are four principal groups of boarding:

Type	Pretreatment
1. Plywood; blockboard; chipboard	Dry abrade with F2 glasspaper and remove dust
2. Hardboard (interior use)	If this material is abraded the smooth surface is destroyed. Remove dust and, regardless of finish, seal with thinned emulsion paint
3. Plasterboard	Plasterboard nailed to timber framing and used as partition walls is known as Dry Lining. It is used in a similar way on ceilings. All joints and angles must be filled with plaster filler and covered with paper tape adhered with the filler. When dry the tape is caulked with filler to feather the thickness of the tape (Fig. 34). Nail heads must be filled also. Seal with thinned emulsion paint.
4. Insulating board (soft fibre board)	Sometimes used in similar way as plasterboard. Treat as plasterboard.

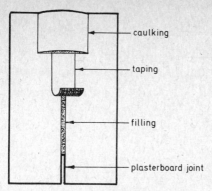

Fig. 34. Caulking joints in plasterboard

Is it necessary to paint zinc, aluminium, lead or copper?

Any of these non-ferrous metals used inside a building will not deteriorate appreciably and, therefore, do not need paint to protect them. When used outside these metals corrode very slowly and quickly lose their sheen but remain effective for many years without painting.

If the natural colour of the metal does not suit the prevailing colour scheme, or if the appearance is unsightly due to staining or tarnishing, non-ferrous metals can be painted. Tarnishing can be prevented by cleaning the metal and applying a spirit lacquer or varnish.

What pretreatments do non-ferrous metals require before painting?

The various treatments are listed in the table below.

Type	Pretreatment	Primer
Aluminium	Remove grease and slightly etch surface with white spirit applied with fine steel wool or emery cloth. Clean surface with rag. Prime immediately	Etch primer and/ or zinc chromate primer

Zinc	Remove grease and slightly etch surface with white spirit applied with fine steel wool or emery cloth. Clean surface with rag. Prime immediately	Zinc chromate
Lead	Remove grease and slightly etch surface with white spirit applied with fine steel wool or emery cloth. Clean surface with rag. Prime immediately	Etch primer or gloss paint direct
Copper	Remove grease and slightly etch surface with white spirit applied with fine steel wool or emery cloth. Clean surface with rag. Prime immediately	Etch primer and aluminium paint or gloss paint direct
Galvanised iron	Remove grease with white spirit. Clean with rag.	Calcium plumbate

What happens if paint is applied over rust?

If the rust is thick the paint will flake. A thin layer of rust will initially cause staining and eventually flaking because paint will not stop the rust continuing to form under the film.

Staining and flaking will occur very rapidly on outside surfaces or those exposed to wet conditions inside a building.

How can rust be removed?

Many methods are employed depending upon the degree of corrosion, size of the area, thickness of steel, type of finish to be used and the nature of the site.

The methods most commonly employed in domestic decoration are as follows. They may be used individually or in combination.

Method	Example
Wire brushing and scraping	Small areas with minimum degree of rust, e.g. metal gutters, wrought iron gates, railings.
Heating and chipping with hammer	Heavy gauge metal with thick scaley rust, e.g. severely neglected cast iron pipes, angle iron supports.
Cold phosphating (application of proprietary phosphoric acid solution)	Small areas of thin rust, e.g. steel clad doors, window frames.

The following methods are specialist processes and their use is limited to large industrial work.

Pneumatic needle gun	Rivetted and bolted steelwork.
Flame cleaning	Gas holders and bridges;
Abrasive blasting	Dockyard equipment, ships and storage tanks

How is plastic and fibreglass prepared for painting?

The surface must be thoroughly clean and free from grease by washing with strong detergent or white spirit. A slight etching of the surface during washing with 400 grade wet or dry paper or fine steel wool will help the paint to adhere.

The best primer is thinned alkyd gloss paint which adheres well to non-absorbent surfaces.

Before painting moulded fibreglass, the washing process must be carried out with particular care to ensure that all traces of the release agent which is applied to make sure that the plastic does not stick to the mould is completely removed. Paint will quickly flake off, if the surface is not scrupulously clean.

Can glass and glazed tiles be painted effectively?

Yes, providing the surface is thoroughly cleaned of dirt and grease. Very thorough washing with strong detergent, followed by rinsing with clean water usually removes all traces of grease. If all the grease has been removed by the detergent, the rinsing water should wet the surface completely. If water does not run easily over parts of the surface this may indicate that traces of grease remain.

The joints between glazed tiles may be absorbent and hold grease and dirt. Therefore, they should be given special treatment, after the general washing, by being rubbed with a strong solvent like cellulose thinners, solvent naptha or methylated spirit. Immediately the surface is dry it must be primed with a paint having excellent adhesive properties, such as thinned alkyd gloss paint. Some manufacturers supply special bonders for glazed tiles.

What is the purpose of the first coat of paint on a bare surface?

The entire life of the paint system is dependent upon the correct type of paint being applied to a correctly prepared surface. The first coat of paint applied to any new or bare surface is called a primer and its function is to penetrate or adhere to the substrate so effectively that it will withstand the weight and tensions exerted by all subsequent coats of paint.

Primers applied to very absorbent surfaces, such as plaster and boarding, are often referred to as sealers because they penetrate slightly to form a bond with the substrate and seal its porosity so that subsequent coats are not absorbed into the material. Sealers are also applied to surfaces which may harm subsequent coatings, such as:

Bituminous surfaces which bleed through oil paints;

Hardwoods like teak whose natural oiliness may prevent paints drying;

Concrete and cement renderings which contain lime and when wet may destroy oil paints.

It is not only the face of structural parts of a building which require painting. Metal and timber components should be primed on all faces before they are fitted into a building so that any part which comes in contact with a wall is protected from the moisture that the wall may contain. The moisture may cause timber to rot and steel to corrode. This complete priming is sometimes referred to as 'back priming'.

The most absorbent part of timber is the end grain. These areas must receive two or three coats of primer in order to reduce their porosity.

What types of primer are available?

Primers must be selected to suit the type and siting of the substrate and the type of finish to be used. The most common types are:

Type	Use	Comments
White or pink wood primer	External and interior timber	Suitable for all timber surfaces
Aluminium wood primer	Hardwoods and resinous surfaces	Excellent sealing properties. Efficient on external hardwood sills
Acrylic wood primer	Interior timber	Water thinned. Quick drying
Calcium plumbate primer	Hardwoods and softwoods Galvanised iron and steel	Contains lead Must not be used on aluminium
Red lead primer	External iron and steel	Contains lead. Can be effective over metal with slight rusting. Must not be used on aluminium
Zinc chromate	Iron and steel and most non-ferrous metals	Safe to use in all situations

Red oxide/zinc chromate	Iron and steel	Cheaper than zinc chromate and produces a thicker film. Less rust inhibitive
Etch primer	Most non-ferrous metals	Thin coating containing an acid which slightly etches metal for good adhesion. Usually requires a zinc chromate primer over it
Alkali resisting primer/sealer	New dry plaster, concrete, asbestos cement, rendering	Either transparent or containing very little pigment
Boarding primer	Hardboard, insulating board, plasterboard	Water thinned Similar composition to emulsion paint

Is there an universal primer?

Some manufacturers produce primers which they state can be used on all surfaces. Being a compromise they are not as effective as the specific primers.

These primers are not always rust inhibitive and they do not have the essential sealing properties required on resinous timber or surfaces containing cement.

Is it possible to give protection to hardwoods without painting?

Yes. There are many transparent coatings which will provide durable films that both enhance the grain markings and seal the wood to reduce its porosity and increase its washability. The natural grain and colour of hardwoods is most decorative and painting them is necessary only when the surface is badly damaged or severely stained.

What types of clear finishes are available?

These range from traditional varnishes to plastics-based finishes. Their various properties and uses are given below.

Name	Principal properties	Uses
Oil varnish	Slow drying (8 hours) Elastic film High-gloss	Exterior and interior surfaces, particularly in exposed positions
Eggshell oil varnish	Poor flow (should be stippled) Yellow Limited washability	Interior surfaces only
Polyurethane varnish (one pack)	Dry within four hours Hard elastic film Available in gloss, eggshell and matt finishes	Exterior and interior surfaces, particularly those required to be used shortly after application
Polyurethane clear finish (2 pack)	Catalysed coating Abrasion, water and chemical resistant Very expensive	Floors Worktops and counters External doors
French polish (and button polish)	Dark colour High gloss Brittle, non waterproof film Requires special skill to apply	Interior doors and counters
Emulsion glaze	Non-yellowing Slightly porous	Interior wall cladding Wallpapers

In general, clear coatings are less durable than paint coatings. The minimum number of coats recommended for effective sealing is as follows:

Exterior surfaces	4 coats
Interior surfaces	2 coats

31

How are hardwoods treated before clear finishing?

The procedures for treating hardwood surfaces are listed below.

Surfaces	Procedure
1. Coated timber in good condition to be recoated with similar material	1. Wash with detergent and wet abrade with 320 silicon carbide paper 2. Dry thoroughly and recoat
2a. Coated timber which is cracking, flaking or blistering to be recoated with any material and 2b. Coated timber which is to be recoated with a different material	1. Strip all coatings with solvent paint paint remover 2. Scour surface with steel wool 3. Rinse off paint remover debris with water or white spirit (read manufacturers instructions) 4. Dry thoroughly
3a. New untreated timber and 3b. Old timber completely stripped off coatings	1. If stained or too dark treat with proprietary wood bleach (follow manufacturers instructions carefully) 2. When dry, dry abrade to level grain with glasspaper or garnet paper used in the direction of the grain. Fine finishing sander should be used on large areas 3. Stop nail holes, deep cracks and damaged areas with plastic wood or resin stopper tinted to the colour of the wood 4. If necessary fill grain with proprietary grain filler tinted to the timber colour and applied by filling knife or rag 5. Dry abrade fillers and stoppers when completely dry

6. If timber is too light or the wrong colour apply wood stain liberally with rag or brush and remove surplus immediately with clean rag

7. When stain is dry apply first coat of clear finish thinned with 50% of its solvent

Are wood stains the same as wood preservatives?

No. Wood stains are dye solutions applied to bare timber to darken them or change their colour. Some contain strong solvents which may have a slight preservative quality but it is not their main function.

Wood preservatives are applied to timbers which generally are not required to be painted, such as roof and floor timbers, and garden fences. Their function is to prevent the timber being attacked by wet or dry rot, or by wood boring insects. Creosote is naturally coloured. Most of the others are available clear for timber which may be seen or coloured for identification purposes.

The types of stains are:

Type	Use	Qualities
Spirit stain or wood dye	All types of internal and external timber surfaces, under varnishes and french polish	Deep penetration Quick drying Wide range of colours (can be mixed together to produce exact matches)
Water stain	Internal surfaces under any clear finish	Quick drying Not dissolved by subsequent coatings Inclined to roughen timber by raising the grain Cheaper than spirit stain

33

The types of wood preservatives are:

Type	Use	Qualities
Coal tar oil (Creosote)	External timbers, e.g. sheds, fences	Dark brown in colour High odour Limited water resistance Cheap
Organic solvent	Exterior wood cladding	Low odour Preserves against insects and fungus Does not rub off
Waterborne	Internal and external timber	Low odour Penetrates damp timber Toxic to fungal spores

Can wood preservatives be coated?

All wood preservatives can be recoated with the same coating without problems. Most of them can be coated over with emulsion paint without the risk of bleeding. A small test should be carried out before a large area is coated.

Oil paint systems can be applied over organic solvent and water borne preservatives although some tend to slow or stop oil paint from drying. A small test will find out which ones have this effect.

If oil paints are applied over creosote-treated timber the paint will be severely discoloured and may remain soft for a long time. This may be prevented by coating the entire surface with aluminium spirit sealer or bitumen sealer.

In what circumstances should old paint be removed?

Paint removal is expensive both in the processes of removal and the subsequent preparatory processes to rebuild the surface.

Therefore it should be carried out only when the old system is in poor condition, and perhaps when changing the type of coating or a dramatic colour change (e.g. red to white).

If the old paint system is flaking, severely blistering or cracking (exposing the primer or substrate) or saponifying, complete removal is necessary. Also when the old coatings are very thick (2 to 3 mm) they become brittle and are easily chipped. Therefore they should be removed completely if a durable and satisfying finish is required.

What methods are there to remove old paint coatings?

There is a variety of methods which can be used. Their advantages and disadvantages are given below.

Type	Use	Quality
Burning off (Paraffin blow-lamp; Gas torch)	Any thickness of paint coatings from timber and iron	Fast Cheap Hazardous on plaster, brick, stone, non-ferrous metals
Spirit paint remover	All types of surfaces except some plastics	Slow on absorbent surfaces and for thick coatings Expensive Messy Water or spirit removeable May harm skin
Caustic soda	Iron and steel surfaces	Softens oil paint only Extremely corrosive to skin and eyes Difficult to remove from absorbent surfaces Dissolves aluminium Cheap

35

Dry abrasion (Disc sander)	Timber surfaces	May damage surface Difficult to get into angles and corners Creates excessive dust
Needle gun or chipping hammer	Thick coatings from iron and steel, brick and concrete	Slow Noisy May damage surface Expensive equipment
Stripping knives; wire brushes; stiff brushes	Loose, flaking and powdering coatings from brick, concrete, rendering	Cheap

What are the hazards involved in paint removal?

Whatever method is used, great care must be taken. The precautions which are necessary are given below.

Burning off	Adjoining flammable surfaces must be protected or removed. Protective non-flammable plates must be laid on floor to catch burning debris. Ventilation is necessary to replace oxygen burnt by the torch. All debris must be removed from the building immediately the job is completed or each day before the site is vacated. Buckets of water should be immediately available.
Spirit paint remover	Do not use near a naked flame as the vapours when burnt may produce a toxic gas (some are flammable and may cause an explosion). Do not smoke while using. Ventilation must be maintained to ensure that air is not replaced by solvent fumes which could cause asphyxia. Protect adjoining surfaces from splashes. Plastics may be softened by the solvent. Hands and eyes should be protected against splashing which may cause inflamation.

Caustic soda	Protect eyes, face, hands and clothing against severe corrosive effect. Protect adjoining areas. Will destroy aluminium.
Dry abrasion	Protect eyes from dust with goggles. Protect nose and throat from dust with face mask. Screen working areas to prevent excessive dust distribution.
Chipping	Protect eyes, nose and throat from dust. Protect ears against noise with ear muffs. Work in short spells to minimise risk of vibration affecting grip.

Is the treatment for stripped surfaces different to that of new surfaces?

No. Once a substrate has been exposed, its qualities and characteristics are similar to that of an untreated material.

How should old painted surfaces in good condition be prepared for repainting?

Ideally old paint coatings should be free from dirt, grease, high gloss, runs and bittiness from previous applications in order to provide good adhesion for subsequent coatings. This can be achieved by washing with detergent, wet abrasion and thorough rinsing.

How can the type of old coating be identified?

Usually it is necessary only to decide whether a surface is absorbent or non-absorbent before redecoration is planned. Absorbent coatings generally are water borne.

Soft distempers and oil-bound distemper or water paint are coatings rarely available today but many old buildings may be coated with them. They can be identified by touching with a damp sponge when they will readily absorb the water and darken slightly. Non-absorbent surfaces, such as oil paints, will remain wet.

If the coating is absorbent its degree of binding to the surface should be checked by rubbing the wet patch with the sponge. If the coating is removed easily it has poor adhesion and must be completely removed by washing before repainting. Emulsion paints may prove to be absorbent but not loosely bound. Size distemper and oil-bound distemper will not be well bound.

What materials are suitable for washing surfaces?

These are listed below.

Type	Use	Qualities
Sugar soap	All types of old coatings	Degreases Slightly etches old coating Cheap Must be thoroughly rinsed
Washing soda	All types of old coatings	Degreases Very cheap Requires considerable scrubbing to be effective
Detergent	All types of old coatings	Extremely efficient degreaser More expensive than above
White spirit	Heavy grease. Metal surfaces which may rust with a water based cleanser	Excellent degreaser Non-corrosive
Industrial degreaser	Thick coatings of grease or deep impregnation of old grease	Deep penetration Water rinsable Excellent degreaser

What materials are suitable for abrading surfaces?

Glasspapers; garnet papers; emery cloth; aluminium oxide paper; silicon carbide steel wool. Full details of the best uses for these materials are given in the table below.

Type	Grade	Uses	Characteristics
Glasspaper	0 1	Denibbing between coats of paint or varnish	Dry abrading only Tends to scratch
	F1 + F2	Smoothing wood and plaster	Clogs readily
	M1 + M2	Smoothing rough wood	Cheap
Garnet	40 – 100	Hand or mechanical abrading of timber to even extreme roughness	Dry abrading only Sharp cutting edge More expensive than glasspaper
	150 – 240	Hand or mechanical finishing of timber and between coats	Orange colour
Aluminium oxide paper	40 – 120 150 – 240	Similar uses as garnet	Dry abrading only Very sharp cutting edge Brown colour
Silicon carbide paper (wet or dry)	180	Hand and mechanical abrading of coarse paintwork	Can be used wet Tough
	320	Removing gloss before repainting	Non-clogging
	400 600	Fine abrasion between coats of paint or varnish	Can be self-lubricating Controlled scratching Black colour

Emery cloth	Coarse Medium Fine	Etching and cleaning metals before painting or lacquering	Dry abrading only Very coarse cutting edge Expensive Tough
Steel wool	Coarse Medium Fine	Degreasing and etching metal and plastic Scouring timber after stripping Flatting varnish	Hands must be protected by gloves Cheap Must be carefully cleaned from surface to prevent rust spotting

What is spot priming?

This is also referred to as 'touching up' or 'touch priming'.

If, during preparation of a previously painted surface, the substrate is exposed it must be primed before any further repainting begins. The primer should invade the surrounding paint system by 4 or 5 mm to ensure that the edge is thoroughly sealed.

These terms can be applied to other coats such as undercoat and finish.

What is making good?

The repairing or smoothing of surfaces before undercoating or finishing paints are applied. There are two principal types:

(a) *Stopper* which is applied to deep holes or cracks or the repair of angles.
(b) *Filler* a thinner material which is rarely applied thicker than 1mm to fill timber grain, fine surface scratches, or small indentations.

40

What types of stopper are available?

These are listed in the following table.

Type	Form	Use	Characteristics
Sand and cement	Dry mixture of 4 parts sand to 1 part cement converted to a thick consistency with water	Deep holes in plaster. Deep holes and angles in external rendering and brickwork	Alkaline Slow setting Does not crack Coarse finish Very strong
Plaster	Plaster of paris or Sirapite added to cold water to a stiff consistency	Deep holes in plaster. Joints between boards on dry lining	Quick setting Cheap If mixed with sand for filling deep holes cracking may be avoided.
Hard stopper	Either a mixture of white lead, whiting and gold size, or proprietary brand (sold in kilogrammes)	Deep holes, cracks or gaps in timber (applied after priming)	Slow setting Elastic Good adhesion Little shrinkage Durable on exposed surfaces
Plastic wood	Ready mixed with cellulose base	Holes and cracks in wood under clear finishing	Quick setting Can be tinted to match wood.
2-Pack stopper	Two components mixed together just before use, based on polyester	Repairing angles, mouldings in joinery and metal	Very quick setting Expensive Very hard finish

41

Mastic	In tubes or refills for caulking gun. Oil based	Gaps between doors or windows and wall	Slow setting Very flexible Very sticky Usually applied with caulking gun
Waterproof joint sealer	In tubes or strips white or coloured Plastic based	Gaps around baths, sinks, basins	Very flexible Excellent adhesion Quick setting Water resisting Expensive

What types of filler are available?

These are as follows:

Type	Form	Use	Characteristics
Plaster based	Dry form in packets mixed with water just before use	Shallow holes and cracks in plaster Timber grain	Quick setting Very absorbent when dry Tends to crack in deep holes
Plaster/ Cellulose based	Dry form in packets mixed with water just before use	Shallow holes and cracks in plaster Timber grain	Slower setting Absorbent when dry Good adhesion
Vinyl based	Ready mixed in plastic containers	Shallow holes and cracks in plaster	Smooth paste Shrinks on drying More expensive than above Absorbent when dry Good adhesion

Vinyl grain filler	Ready mixed in plastic containers	Surface cracks in timber grain for internal and external use	Smooth paste Quick setting Absorbent when dry Finely ground Clear or brown colour
Oil based paste filler	Ready mixed in tins	Surface cracks and indentations on internal and external timber surface	Slow drying Low absorption when dry Shrinks on drying Can be wet flatted Applied to primed or painted surfaces only

How is an arris or moulding repaired?

Various types of stopper are used for this work:

Internal cornices — Plaster of Paris

External cornices }
Stone surrounds } Sand and cement mixture

Door or window edges }
Sill angles } 2-pack resin stopper
Skirting or architrave edges }

The setting time of plaster of paris can be increased by mixing it with glue size instead of water.

Edge repair (see Figs. 35–38)

1. Clean area free from loose material (Fig. 35).
2. Fix smooth timber, metal or plastic rule to one side of angle with front edge flush with angle (Fig. 36).
3. Push stopper into hole and smooth off flush with rule or knife (Fig. 37).
4. After initial set, remove rule and fill in any holes (Fig. 38).

43

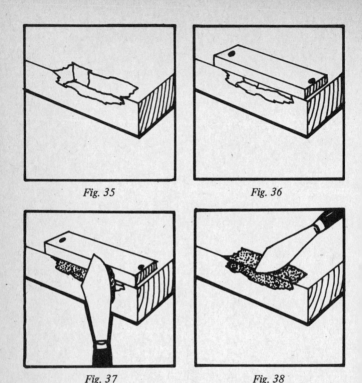

Fig. 35

Fig. 36

Fig. 37

Fig. 38

Figs. 35–38. Sequence for edge repair of doors or windows

Moulding repair (see Figs. 39–42)

Cut a template of the moulding shape from card or thin plastic.

1. Clean area free from loose material (Fig. 39).
2. Place an excess of stopper into damaged area (Fig. 40).
3. Immediately drag template through wet stopper to push into hole and remove surplus (Fig. 41).
4. Repeat process until smooth. Clean off surplus. Fill any holes (Fig. 42).

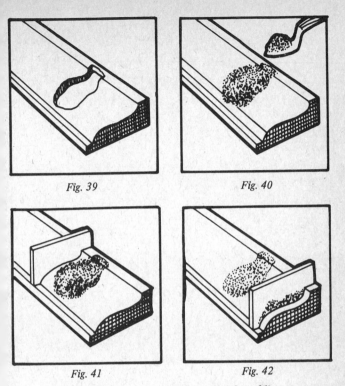

Fig. 39   Fig. 40

Fig. 41   Fig. 42

Figs 39–42. Sequence for the repair of mouldings

Mouldings can be repaired also by the use of small wood or metal modelling tools. After an excess of stopper has been placed in hole and allowed to set to a plastic state it can be modelled to fit the contour with the modelling tools.

How are fillers and stoppers applied?

With a filling or stopping knife. Use sufficient pressure to bend the knife blade considerably and to push the material deep

45

into the indents. The surplus filler is removed flush with the surface by pulling the cleaned knife blade over the surface at approximately right angles.

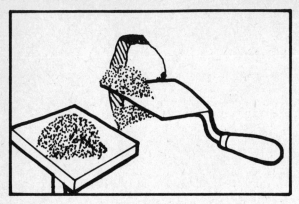

Fig. 43. A pointing trowel is used to fill cracks with plaster or sand and cement

Deep holes and cracks should be first raked out with a knife, chisel or shave hook to remove loose material. Whenever possible, the edge of the crack should be undercut to ensure a tighter fit. When using plaster or sand and cement a pointing trowel is often used to apply them (Fig. 43).

What treatment do fillers require when dry?

Where necessary, the making good should be abraded smooth. Oil-based fillers should be wet abraded, all others need to be abraded dry.

Plaster and plaster based fillers are very absorbent and must be sealed with plaster sealer or emulsion paint before the surface is painted, otherwise a patchy finish will result. Oil-based fillers are not so absorbent but they will need to be undercoated before a gloss finish is applied, otherwise sinkage will occur.

How many coats of paint are necessary?

On new or bare surfaces the minimum is a two coat system for interior surfaces and three coat system for exterior work. When referring to two or three coat systems it is generally accepted to mean two or three coats over primer.

Therefore typical minimum paint systems are:

2 coat work	Primer, undercoat, gloss finish
3 coat work	Primer, undercoat, 2 coats gloss finish or Primer, 2 coats undercoat, gloss finish.

If the surfaces are in very exposed situations (facing south or not protected from any weather) or likely to be constantly knocked, rubbed against or wetted by condensation at least one extra coat should be applied.

Exposed iron and steel requires at least five coats of paint to ensure that all the 'peaks' of the metal are adequately coated. Otherwise the thinly covered areas will soon rust and the entire film will quickly break down.

For surfaces which are painted primarily for decoration, i.e. ceilings, plaster walls, exterior walls, the number of coats necessary depends on the opacity of the paint being used. The coating should appear of even colour and sheen with no substrate grinning through. Most whites and tints will cover in two coats over a sealed surface. Strong colours such as bright yellow, orange and red may need three or four coats before an opaque finish is obtained.

Thixotropic paints generally allow a thicker coating to be applied, therefore not so many coats are necessary. They are not so opaque on edges or narrow areas as on large flat uninterrupted surfaces.

What coatings need thinning with methylated spirits?

1. Shellac knotting for treating knots and resinous areas before priming.
2. French polish and button polish as clear coatings for interior timbers.
   Most other coatings are thinned with water or white spirit.

What is thixotropic paint?

A paint made very thick like a jelly. It has a special property of becoming thin when stirred or brushed but quickly reverts to a jelly when left to stand. Providing the paint is not brushed out too much or too quickly, thixotropic paints allow thicker films to be applied.

Paints available in this form include emulsion, eggshell and gloss finishes.

How do alkyd and polyurethane paints differ?

They contain completely different synthetic resins.

Alkyd is the name of a synthetic resin used in most under-coats and gloss finishes on the market today. It is very good for interior and exterior work and is also used in eggshell paints for interior use.

True polyurethanes are 'two-pack' materials which dry by a chemical reaction within hours of the two components being mixed. They are hard wearing, water resistant, expensive and can prove a health hazard during application.

It is possible to react polyurethane resins with drying oils to produce one-pack polyurethanes, these have similar applica-tion properties to alkyd gloss paints and often have slightly better resistance to heat, knocks, scratches and stains but in most cases alkyd gloss finishes have better external durability.

Some manufacturers incorporate a small quantity of poly-urethane in alkyd paints to make them a little more knock, scratch and stain resistant but the degree to which this small addition improves these properties is very limited.

Do all white paints yellow?

No. Paints based on linseed oil media tend to yellow when the surface is excluded from light, e.g. inside cupboard doors and behind pictures. The yellowing will sometimes bleach out if exposed to light.

Some resins are particularly prone to yellowing i.e. phenolic resins, but most of the decorative paints on the market today do not yellow to any great extent. The resins used in emulsion paints do not yellow.

Can gloss paints be effectively applied over any other coatings?

Providing the surface is in sound condition e.g. not flaking, cracking or blistering, is clean and abraded to provide a key, then standard decorative gloss paints can be applied over many other types of surface coatings such as emulsion paint, water thinned paints, eggshell and flat finishes, cellulose finishes, varnishes. They can be applied over primers but full gloss, adhesion and hiding power is likely to suffer if this is done.

For best results, gloss finishes should be applied over the appropriate undercoat formulated especially for the job.

Are undercoats always necessary?

The purpose of an undercoat is to cover up or hide the surface to which it is applied. It also helps to build up a film thickness, provide an even surface porosity, a key for subsequent coats and a colour close to that of the finishing paint. In most cases, therefore, if good appearance and a durable finish is required then undercoats are necessary.

If a job is to be repainted the same colour and the surface is perfectly sound with no trace of any breakdown or damage of the finish and a good film thickness has previously been built up, then the surface can be flatted and a further coat of gloss applied direct.

Some manufacturers recommend two coats of finish. Providing a good surface has already been achieved two coats of gloss can improve flexibility, depth of gloss and durability.

What are the ideal drying conditions for paint?

Clean dry and warm air.

Dampness or humidity will slow down the evaporation of the solvents and in severe cases slow down and even stop the paint drying. Cold conditions, around 5°C or less make paints thicken up and difficult to apply. The solvents are slow to evaporate and the paint can be very slow drying.

Above 20°C the solvents evaporate quickly causing the paint to set up rapidly. This makes them difficult to apply and can cause the paint to shrivel and wrinkle.

Good ventilation is necessary to take away the solvents as they evaporate. Rain, heavy condensation or dew falling on a wet paint film can cause rain spotting or cratering which spoils the finish. One of any combination of these can affect the appearance and durability of a paint film.

Is there a special technique for applying primer?

Most primers are best applied by brush to plaster, timber, iron and steel. The action of the brush helps to remove pockets of air, and force the primer into the surface. A brush may have to be used to 'punch' the paint into crevices, angles and indentations to ensure that there are no misses. Areas missed means that a particular spot is not sealed or protected.

Coarse brush marks will show through and spoil a finish, expecially if the primer is not laid off correctly.

Film thickness is also important particularly with rust inhibiting primers. If primers are thinned out too much or brushed out to a very thin film then the life of every subsequent coat of paint can be affected.

Some quick drying primers have to be sprayed. It is always advisable to follow the manufacturers recommendations.

How can brushmarks be avoided when applying undercoats?

First apply a full and even coat of paint. Immediately lay it off firm and straight in one direction followed by a light laying off in the opposite direction using the tip of the brush.

This process must be completed before the paint begins to set otherwise it will not flow out and leave coarse brushmarks.

How are eggshell paints, emulsion paints and undercoatings brush applied?

All paints must be applied in an even film.

Undercoats are layed-off straight generally in the direction of the grain, or vertically on walls (Fig. 44). Eggshell and emulsion paints are brushed criss-crossed, sometimes known as scatter brushing (Fig. 45).

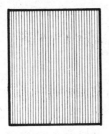 

Laying off vertically   Laying off with grain

Fig. 44. Undercoats should be layed-off straight in the direction of the grain. On walls the undercoat should be applied vertically

Criss cross laying off

Fig. 45. Criss-cross application (or scatter brushing) used for eggshell and emulsion paints

51

How can runs in gloss paint be avoided?

The main cause of runs in gloss finish is not applying the paint evenly. Gloss paint must be crossed in different directions until the paint is distributed evenly over the surface. Finally on large panels, flush doors and wall areas it should be layed-off firmly and vertically or, in the case of frames, with the grain (Fig. 46).

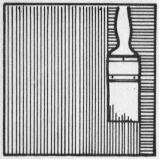

Fig. 46. When painting a flat surface gloss paint should be layed-off vertically

It is also important to brush out and lay-off a reasonably large area as it is impossible to obtain an even film thickness over a whole area or section if it is coated in small pieces.

Note thixotropic paints should be applied in small areas at a time, taking care not to over brush.

Special care must be taken when coating surfaces with protrusions or mouldings as paint can build up around screw heads, nuts, bolts and in quirks of mouldings causing runs or tears.

Is the technique of varnishing similar to that of gloss painting?

Yes. Surface preparation however must be perfect, as any blemishes on the surface will be emphasised once the varnish is applied, then the surface is sealed and mistakes cannot be rectified without stripping back to the substrate.

When is a paint roller more effective than a brush?

This decision depends on:

Size. When painting an area less than about 6 to 8m^2, it may take longer to clean the roller than the time saved in application. On larger wall and ceiling areas a roller can apply paint twice as fast as a brush.

Shape. On an area less than the width of a roller all cutting in has to be done by brush. Therefore, if a job has mostly small areas and a great deal of cutting in then a brush is usually quicker.

Textures. When coating a surface with a texture such as ingrain and Anaglypta papers, short and medium pile rollers will reach into the bottom of the texture while a brush has to be punched or pushed in.

Type of paint. Most paints can be easily applied by roller. A few, which are quick setting, pull on the roller and a good finish cannot be achieved.

Type of finish. When paint is applied by roller, in almost every case a textured finish is obtained, commonly known as 'Orange-peel'. If gloss paint is applied correctly this is hardly discernable. At the other extreme, heavy emulsion paints usually have a pronounced orange peel finish. These textures are usually quite acceptable and very seldom is the use of a roller ruled out because of this.

What are the techniques to ensure good cutting in?

Cutting in is the clean painting of angles, glazing bars and to a line. It requires considerable skill and practice and can be helped by:

(a) Using a good brush, well broken in preferably shaped towards a point, or special cutting-in tool (Fig. 47).

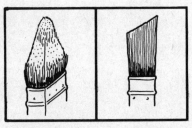

Broken in brush   Cutting in tool

Fig. 47. A cutting-in tool or broken-in brush can be used for painting to a line

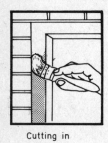

Fig. 48. When cutting-in, use long straight flowing strokes along the line

Cutting in

(b) Charging the brush with excess paint removed by tapping (not scraping) on the side of the kettle.
(c) Using the edge of the brush, not the flat.
(d) Applying long straight flowing strokes along the line or edge, not short jabs (Fig. 48).

How soon can a second coat of paint be applied?

When the film can be handled and shows no sign of being soft or cheesy. The time this takes depends entirely on the type of paint and the conditions under which it is drying.

Most oil/resin paints should be left overnight while emulsion paints and water thinned coatings can usually be overcoated after 3—4 hours (see manufacturers instructions).

Cold and damp weather conditions will slow the drying process of all paints and, in several cases, will stop drying.

What treatment is necessary between coats of paint?

In many cases it is sufficient to denib with fine or partly worn glasspaper to remove any dust or dirt in the dry paint film. The surface must then be dusted off to remove the powder and dust before applying the finish coat.

If a glass-like finish is required, the surface must be wet flatted with a wet-or-dry abrasive paper until the surface is perfectly smooth and matt. In place of a dusting brush, a tack rag should be used to remove every particle of dust from the surface just before applying the paint. If coatings are left for a period between coats and a layer of dirt has gathered on the surface this must be removed preferably by washing off before repainting. Wet flatting may also be required to improve adhesion.

Dust trapped between coats of paint can reduce the durability and seriously affect the appearance of the finish.

Is it necessary to provide good ventilation when preparing surfaces and applying paint?

When preparing surfaces dust and fumes are produced. Good ventilation helps to reduce the chances of inhaling these. Where possible it is also advisable to:

(a) Use wet abrading processes.

(b) Wear a face mask.

(c) Remove excessive dust with an industrial vacuum cleaner rather than sweeping.

Fumes are also produced when liquid paint removers and burning-off equipment are used and good ventilation is very important.

All paints contain solvents, mainly white spirit or water and these must evaporate before a paint can dry. As they evaporate, spirit solvents can cause irritation to the nose and throat particularly if allowed to build up in high concentrations.

What paints are suitable for hot water radiators and pipes?

Normal gloss paints will stand up to 90°C which is well above the temperature of most hot water systems. White and pale colours may yellow over 70°C. For steam and super heated systems manufacturers advice should be taken.

As undercoats tend to become brittle on heating, it is often advisable to apply two coats of gloss which provide a more flexible film than one undercoat and one coat of gloss.

Should paints be thinned?

Only according to manufacturers instructions.

Paints are usually made ready for use and thinning should only be carried out to meet special requirements for example painting very porous surfaces. Thinning a paint may make it easier and faster to apply but the result will be a thinner film thickness, reduced durability, poor gloss and less resistance to abrasion.

Paints can become increasingly viscous as they get colder and more difficult to apply. In this case they can either be warmed or, if this is not possible, a very small quantity of thinners can be added to make the paint workable.

Most paints require thinning if they are to be sprayed.

Can different types of paint be mixed together effectively?

Paints of different film formers cannot be mixed together, e.g. emulsion paint and oil paint.

While it is often possible to mix similar types of paint from one manufacturer, paints from different manufacturers should never be intermixed.

How long will a paint system last?

Providing the surface is sound, clean and abraded, a correct paint system with good quality paint used and if full coats of paint are applied in dry warm weather conditions, then a paint system can last five to six years on exterior work and ten to twenty years or more on interior work.

If any or all these factors are ignored, paint can start breaking down in three months, especially on surfaces exposed to industrial or coastal conditions.

What are the signs that repainting is necessary?

Loss of gloss, chalking and splitting of the paint film on certain critical areas. These are:
  (a) On sills, especially the ends.
  (b) Joints of window frames and sashes.
  (c) The putties especially along the bottom.
  (d) The bottom rails of doors.
  (e) Spots of rust on iron and steel.
Once a paint film shows signs of breaking down it should be repainted. Delay will result in:
  (a) Accelerated breakdown and possibly having to strip all the remaining paint.
  (b) Water penetrating the damaged film, which could cause dry or wet rot in timber and rust on ironwork.

How do you calculate the quantity of paint required?

Most types of paint have different spreading capacities, and it is always advisable to consult the manufacturers instructions.

Thin paints can be spread over larger areas than thick or sticky paints. Textured and absorbent surfaces require much more paint than smooth hard surfaces.

The following are typical of commonly used paints:

Gloss finish	approx 15–17 m^2 per litre
Undercoat	approx 11–13 m^2 per litre
Emulsion paint	approx 14–16 m^2 per litre
Alkali resisting primer on smooth hard plaster	approx 9–11 m^2 per litre
Cement rendering slight texture	approx 7– 9 m^2 per litre
Stucco or rough cast	approx 3– 6 m^2 per litre

Example:
A wall 4 m high by 15 m long will have an area of 60 m^2. If it is to be coated with emulsion paint which has a spreading capacity of 14 m^2 per litre the amount of paint required per coat is:

$$\frac{60}{14} = 4^1/_7 \text{ litres}$$

Therefore it would be necessary to purchase 5 litres.

What pretreatment is necessary for badly cracked ceilings?

Rake out all large cracks undercutting to obtain a key and fill with a plaster filler.

To reinforce the surface the ceiling should then be lined with a special reinforced (linen-backed) lining paper.

How can damp patches on walls be effectively sealed?

The only real answer to this is to find the source of the dampness and repair it.

Common problems are faulty rain-water pipes, gutters, etc, a defective or no damp-proof course (in older buildings) and leaking pipes.

One or two decorative treatments can be used to help but they will never solve the problems. These include:

1. Coating the surface with special bituminous products.
2. Applying lead and aluminium foil, using a thick paint made from thick undercoat and gold size as an adhesive. Joints must always be overlapped.
3. Pitch or waterproof papers applied pitch face to the wall with stout paste.
4. Special foil backed papers applied with the supplied adhesive.

These materials will hold dampness to a limited extent, but they are more effective as barriers against the stains which usually result from dampness.

What types of paint are waterproof?

Many paints will withstand water in the form of rain and snow but would not be suitable for continuous submersion such as coatings for water tanks and swimming pools. All good quality gloss paints are suitable for exterior paintwork on metal, timber, brick and rendered surfaces.

For special conditions, paint manufacturers should be consulted but the type of materials which can be used include:

Chlorinated rubber paints
Epoxy resin paints
Polyurethane coatings
Special bituminous coatings.

How is paint strained?

1. By stretching a piece of old stocking or muslin over a paint kettle tying it in position and pouring sufficient paint into the kettle through the strainer (Fig. 49).

Fig. 49. Paint can be strained by stretching a piece of old stocking or muslin over a paint kettle

Fig. 50. Card and muslin disposable paint strainer

Fig. 51. Metal paint strainer with removable brass wire gauge

2. Using a card and muslin disposable strainer (Fig. 50).
3. Through special metal strainer with a removable brass wire gauge which can be cleaned after use (Fig. 51).

Heavy bodied paints may have to be pushed through the mesh with a small brush.

3

WALLCOVERINGS

When hanging wallpaper should the old wallpaper be stripped?

Yes. The following faults may occur if the old paper is left on:
1. Peeling due to the insecure adhesion of the old paper.
2. Old joins will show through the new paper.
3. Loss of adhesion due to porous nature of old paper.
4. Blistering where old paper is not firmly adhered.
5. Bad joints, as the new paper will not slide into position.
6. Grinning through of old paper pattern when thin papers are used.

How is old wallpaper removed?

The method used is determined by the type of paper and condition of the surface.

Pulps, grounds and embossed papers. In some cases the paper can be stripped off dry by lifting an edge and pulling away in strips leaving odd patches to be removed by wetting. If this method fails then thoroughly wet the surface with hot water and leave to soak until the paper can be removed easily with a stripping knife (Fig. 52). On some papers two or three wettings may be necessary.

A small quantity of liquid detergent or soap powder added to the water will serve as a wetting agent and aid penetration.

Washable wallpapers. The water resistant coating must be scored by scouring with a wire brush. Once the surface is broken, the paper can be soaked as previously described. Some types of washable papers are designed so that they can be removed by peeling away an edge and pulling off each piece.

Any remaining material should be completely removed by washing down and rinsing with clean water.

Vinyls. Lift the corners and pull away the plastic face leaving the base paper on the wall. If firmly adhered it can be left on to act as a lining. A more reliable job will result if the base paper is removed by soaking and the surface relined if required.

Fig. 52. Stripping knife for removing wallpaper

Fig. 53. Using a nail block to score the surface of old painted or varnished wallpapers

Painted or varnished papers. In some instances the tension caused by the drying of the paint may have reduced the bond between the paper and the wall surface, enabling it to be removed dry. If wetting is necessary the surface will have to be carefully scored using a nail block (Fig. 53). Avoid cutting

PREPARATION OF UNTREATED OR NEW SURFACES

Preparation	Plaster	Concrete	Plasterboard Blockboard Chipboard	Hardboard Insulating board
Wash and rinse		x		
Dry scrape	x	x		
Dry abrade	x	x	x	
Touch up nail heads			x	x
Size	x	x	x	x
Apply linen tape over joints and fill edges			x	x
Apply appropriate primer/filler			x	x

PREPARATION OF TREATED SURFACES

Preparation	Emulsion	Oil-bound distemper	T & G boarding* (painted/ varnished)	Oil printed	Papered plaster	Soft distemper
Wash and rinse			x	x		
Remove completely					x	x
Dry scrape	x	x				
Wet abrade			x	x		
Apply sealer		x				
Apply size	x		x	x	x	
Apply lining paper				x		
Apply linen-backed lining paper			x			

* Joints must be filled with plaster filler before sizing

into the plaster as this will lead to excessive making good. Then the paper can be soaked and easily removed.

A wallpaper steam stripper is a useful piece of equipment for this purpose (see Figs. 32 and 33).

How is a surface prepared for papering?

Wallpaper can be applied to any dry and sound surface providing it is properly prepared and filled. The tables on page 63 can be used to identify the preparation required.

What is size?

A clear coating used to even the porosity of the surface. Two types of material can be used.

Glue size. Made from animal glue and sold in granulated powder form. Hot and cold water types are available, the former giving better penetration. Most manufacturers incorporate a fungicidal agent for protection against mould growth.

Cellulose size. Available in powder form to be mixed with cold water for use under cellulose and starch ether pastes. A thinned form of the adhesive can also be used.

What is lining paper and when should it be used?

Lining papers, sometimes referred to as 'preparatory' papers, are used where the underlying surface is in poor condition, or when the finished paper is of a special type that requires the surface to be lined.

What are the types?

White lining. A base paper available in varying weights, e.g. $55g/m^2$ (lightweight) $75g/m^2$ (medium) and $90g/m^2$ (heavy) which provides a uniformly absorbent surface for most wallcoverings. This type is particularly useful on non-porous surfaces or where large areas of making-good have been carried out. The paper should be hung in the opposite direction to the finishing paper to avoid coinciding joints which would cause a weakness.

Reinforced linen-backed lining. Heavy white lining bonded to a fine muslin scrim, used on surfaces subject to excessive movement, e.g. tongued and grooved boarding or badly cracked surfaces.

Pitch papers. A brown lining coated on one side with bitumen and used as a temporary treatment on damp walls. These should be lap jointed with the pitch to the wall.

Metal foil. Normally thin aluminium foil supplied either with a special adhesive or as an 'iron on' type. Lead foil is available also which is adhered with an oil paint. Both are used as a temporary treatment on damp patches. They normally require further lining to provide an absorbent surface.

Expanded polystyrene. Available in thin sheets or rolls of foamed polystyrene. Used for insulating outside walls. They should be butt joined and may require further lining.

What are the types of wallcovering?

There is a wide variety of wallcoverings to suit all tastes. The characteristics of the various types are shown in the table below. The numbers relate to the table on page 68.

Types	*Characteristics and uses*
1. Pulps	Cheap self coloured thin papers. Hang immediately after pasting.
2. Grounds	Coated papers on which the design is printed by hand or machine. A variety of qualities is available. Some grades may need to be left to soak after pasting.
3. Common embosses	Pulps or grounds having a slightly raised texture or pattern. Hang immediately after pasting. Do not use a roller.

4. Duplex	Two thicknesses of paper embossed by metal rollers. Deep textures. Allow to soak after pasting until supple. Do not use a roller.
5. Anaglypta	Duplex paper embossed while glue is wet. Usually white for painting over. Hang as for Duplex.
6. Wet embossed (Supaglypta)	Heavy quality paper moulded while still in pulp form. Usually white for painting over. Hang as for Duplex.
7. Woodchip (ingrain)	Solid back with surface texture of small pieces of wood adhered to the surface. Hang immediately after pasting. It is often painted over.
8. Lincrusta	Putty-like coating applied to paper and textured. Very heavy material. Soak with water before applying adhesive. It is often decorated over.
9. Relief vinyl	Thick p.v.c. coating deeply textured on a paper backing. Hang with special adhesive. It is sometimes decorated over.
10. Washable	Ground or duplex papers coated with p.v.a. glaze so that they can be washed. Hang with fungicide adhesive.
11. Vinyl	Thin p.v.c. film printed or textured and bonded to a paper backing. Washable finish. Hang with special vinyl adhesive only.
12. Ready-pasted	Washable or vinyl paper coated with water active adhesive. Requires soaking in water before hanging.
13. Expanded polystyrene rolls	Improves thermal qualities of walls and ceilings. Highly flammable and easily damaged. Painted or papered over.
14. Expanded polystyrene tiles	High thermal qualities. Highly flammable and easily damaged. Usually decorated with emulsion paint.
15. Foamed plastic (Novamura)	Light to handle. Special adhesive applied to walls.
16. Special coverings	Grasscloth, silk, wool, felt and laminates of metal, cork and plastic. Very expensive. It is essential to follow the manufacturer's instructions.

How can the right type of adhesive be selected?

Check with the manufacturer's instructions given with the wall-covering. The following list gives some of the adhesives which are available and can be used as a guide. The group numbers relate to the table on page 68.

Group 1	Group 2	Group 3
Polycell	Polycell Plus	Polycell H.D.
Rexcell	Cannon Plus	Rex Vinyl
Lapcell		Dulite Vinyl
		Lap Vinyl

Group 4	Group 5	Group 6
Rex Cold Water	Rex Prepared	Dextrine
Lap Cold Water	Octopus Tub	
Tap wata		
Lap Boiling Water		
Octopus Cold Water		
Cannon Cold Water		
Clam Cold Water		

Group 7	Group 8	Group 9
Crown Lincrusta	Clam 143 (ready mixed)	Adpep 281
Glue	Solvite	Adpep 283
	Gloy Special (readymixed)	Tretobond 282
	Square Deal all purpose adhesive	Warmaline Adhesive
	Superlap	

Group 10	Group 11
Ross Bond 100	Polymura
Leyland High Performance	

ADHESIVES FOR WALLCOVERINGS

Types of wallcovering	Adhesives										
	1	2	3	4	5	6	7	8	9	10	11
1	x	x		x	x						
2		x		x	x			x		x	
3		x		x	x			x		x	
4		x		x	x			x		x	
5		x		x	x			x		x	
6		x		x	x			x		x	
7											
8							x				
9						x		x		x	
10		x						x		x	
11			x					x		x	
12											
13			x					x		x	
14									x		
15											x
16								x			

Note. Approximate quantities can be estimated as 1 litre of mixed adhesive per roll of wallpaper. This will vary depending on the user, the type of adhesive and the texture of paper.

What methods are used to determine the quantity of wallpaper or ceiling paper required?

There are three main methods:
1. The following method is useful for irregular shaped areas, e.g. staircase walls, walls with many or unusually large openings etc., or when measuring from drawings.

Draw a plan of area showing position of any features such as doors, windows, cupboards etc. Give each wall a reference letter (Fig. 54).

Take each wall separately and record all dimensions (Fig. 55). A wall this shape should be divided into two units, a

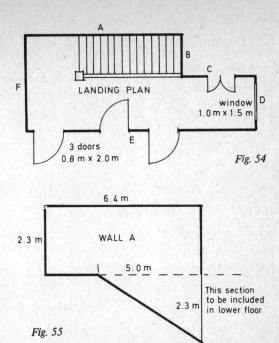

Fig. 54

Fig. 55

Figs. 54 and 55. Use a plan to assist in calculating irregular shaped areas; and record the dimensions of each wall

rectangle and a triangle, the area of each calculated and added together.

Example:

Rectangle = Length x Breadth 6.4 x 2.3 = 14.72m^2
Triangle = ½ base x height = 2.5 x 2.3 = 5.75m^2

Total = 20.47m^2

69

Proceed round all walls in a similar way subtracting areas of doors and windows. When all the walls have been calculated, add them together to obtain the total area to be papered. One roll of standard English wallpaper measures approximately 10.5 m x 0.530 m or 5.326 m^2. For practical measuring purposes this can be rounded off to 5 m^2. Divide the total wall area by 5 and this represents the number of rolls required. To allow for waste in cutting and matching add 1 extra roll for each 7 rolls required.

2. *Rule of thumb method*. This may be used for average rooms where doors and windows are of normal proportion.

Measure the height of the walls and divide into the length of one roll, e.g. from a 10 m long roll of wallpaper 4 lengths can be cut to fit a wall 2.3 m high.

Using a roll of wallpaper, mark off the number of widths required round the room (include doors, etc) then divide by 4 to obtain the required quantity, e.g.

$$28 \text{ widths} \div 4 = 7 \text{ rolls required.}$$

3. Most wallpaper or adhesive manufacturers provide a chart for easy calculation of the number of rolls required. Calculate the perimeter and height of the room and where these dimensions intersect on the chart the number of rolls required is indicated.

What do the terms 'length' and 'piece' mean?

The term length refers to a portion of wallpaper cut to size ready for hanging. This is the height of the wall or length of a ceiling plus approximately 60 mm each end for fitting into angles.

The term 'piece' refers to one full roll of wallpaper before it is cut into lengths.

What steps can be taken to ensure that all the paper used in a room is the same shade?

An identification number is printed on the end of each roll of paper or on the label in the clear wrapping. It is important that all rolls have the same number.

In addition to this, a visual check should be made by comparing the colour of all rolls under good light before cutting. If there is any doubt the supplier should be consulted.

What are 'set' 'drop' and 'non match' patterns?

These are terms used to indicate the type of design used. *'Straight or set' pattern* (Fig. 56). A design that repeats in a horizontal line, the match being at the same level on each edge. *Drop pattern* (Fig. 57). A design which repeats on a diagonal

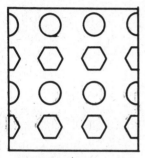

Fig. 56. 'Straight or set' patterns

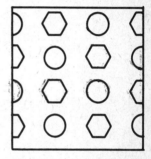

Fig. 57. 'Drop match' pattern

Fig. 58. 'Non-match' or 'random' patterns

71

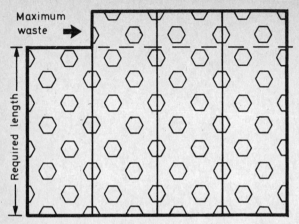

All lengths cut from one roll

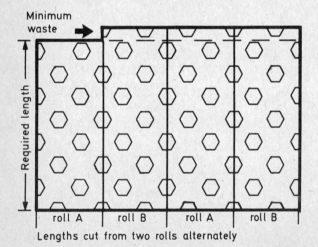

Lengths cut from two rolls alternately

Fig. 59. Method of eliminating waste when using a 'drop pattern' paper

line. The pattern repeats on the same level on alternate lengths only. *'Non-match' or 'random' pattern* (Fig. 58). A design that has no apparent repeat and does not require matching.

How can waste be avoided when using a drop pattern?

It is not possible to avoid waste altogether but it can be cut to a minimum by using two rolls and cutting lengths alternately from each roll. The rolls should be marked A and B respectively on the back each time a length has been cut off. The two illustrations in Fig. 59 show the amount of waste on each length when cutting from one roll, and how waste can be reduced by cutting from alternate rolls.

How many lengths should be cut at one time?

Where possible sufficient lengths to cover one complete wall or room should be cut and matched on the pasteboard at one time. This saves time and reduces the risk of damage to the paper by having to continually offer the roll up to the wall in order to match and mark off each length individually.

When using a drop pattern each length should be marked to avoid mixing them up. Before cutting the rolls, each wall should be measured at both ends and in the middle and the lengths cut to the greater measurement.

Where should the first length be hung when papering a ceiling?

The first consideration should be where the main source of light enters the room. This is usually the wall with the largest window or a window facing south. The first length should then be hung nearest to and parallel with that wall.

In some cases it may be desirable to work from a centre line particularly if the paper has a prominent pattern, this ensures a balanced effect at the edges. An immovable obstruction in the middle of the ceiling can provide a convenient starting point. Fig. 60 shows how to start papering for various shapes of room.

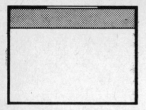

Room with one window

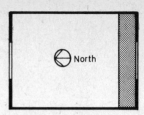

Room with two windows

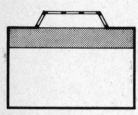

Room with bay or recess

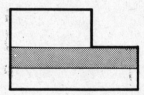

'L' shaped room

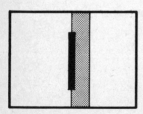

Immovable obstruction

Fig. 60. How to start papering ceilings in various shapes of room

Where should the first length be hung when papering walls?

The first length on every wall must be hung to a plumbed line never to an angle, window or door architrave. Papering normally starts by the window and proceeds away from the light in both directions meeting if possible in an obscure corner.

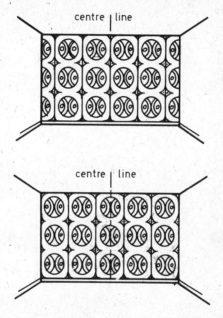

Fig. 61. When using a patterned wallpaper, the first pieces should be hung from the centre line. Two methods of doing this are shown above

When using a paper with a large pattern the chimney breast or other focal wall should be centred and the paper hung from the centre line as shown in Fig. 61.

How is a starting line marked on a ceiling?

Measure the width of the ceiling paper and deduct 5 to 10 mm to allow the paper to lap round the angle at the junction of the wall and ceiling. Mark this distance at each end of the ceiling where the first length is to be hung.

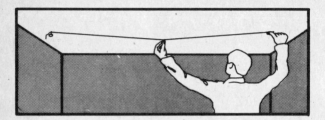

Fig. 62. Striking a chalk line on a ceiling

A chalked line held taut with the aid of a drawing pin between these two marks is pulled away from the surface and allowed to snap back into place depositing a line of chalk on the ceiling (Fig. 62).

A loop knot in the middle helps to locate the line with the free hand, the other hand being used to keep the line taut.

How is the paste applied to the paper?

Paste applied carelessly can result in difficult hanging, loss of adhesion, blistering, staining, overlapping and poor matching.

Use either a special pasting brush or an emulsion brush, preferably worn so that the bristles will spread the paste evenly over the paper. Avoid getting paste onto the table or hands as this may find its way onto the face of the paper.

Position the paper so that it lies along the far edge of the table. Apply paste down the centre then brush out to the far edge spreading evenly. Next, position the paper so that it lies along the near edge of the table, brushing the paste evenly over the lower half. Always brush in an outward direction to avoid

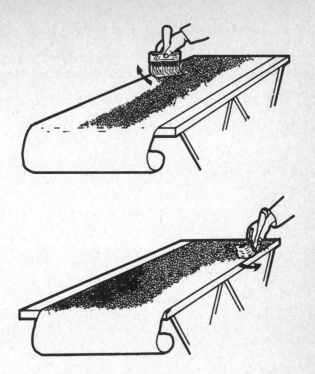

Fig. 63. When pasting paper always brush in an outward direction at the edges

depositing paste on the edge of the table (Fig. 63). Finally check for misses along the edges.

How is the paper folded ready for hanging?

When hanging wall lengths, the paper is folded end to end. With the longest fold at the top or right hand side of the table and the short fold at the bottom of the length (Fig. 64).

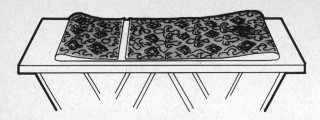

Fig. 64. End to end folding of wallpaper ready for hanging

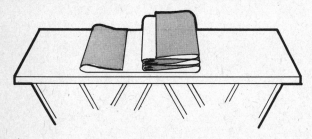

Fig. 65. Ceiling papers should be folded by the concertina method

When hanging ceiling paper or wallpaper horizontally the paper is folded concertina method (Fig. 65). The fold should be about 300 to 400 mm and kept even. A short fold at each end enables the paper to be picked up without getting paste on the hands.

Should the paper be allowed to soak?

This depends on the type of paper and paste used.

Pasted paper should be hung when it is pliable enough to be handled without difficulty but the exact time can only be found with experience and may vary from immediate hanging of thin paper to 15 minutes with heavy embossed type.

Paper defects which can be caused by over-soaking or under-soaking are shown in the table.

PAPER DEFECTS

Defects caused by incorrect soaking	Cause	
	Under soaking	Over soaking
Blistering	X	X
Discolouration		X
Edge springing	X	
Delamination		X
Poor matching	X	X
Tearing		X
Staining		X
Overlapping	X	
Creasing		X

What kind of scaffold is necessary for paperhanging?

The paperhanger should be in a safe, comfortable position with both hands free to handle the paper. Fig. 66 shows examples of how this can be achieved.

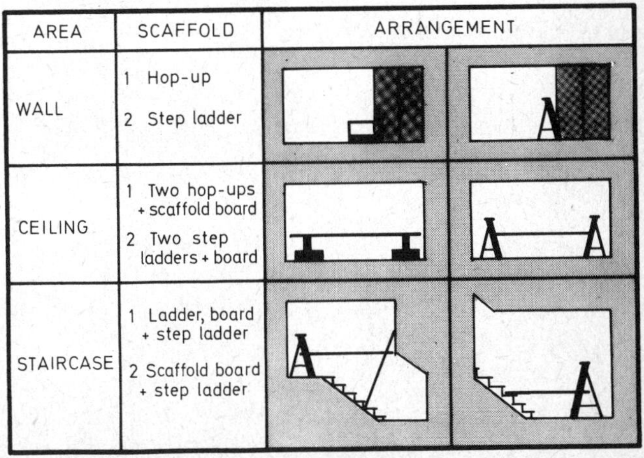

AREA	SCAFFOLD	ARRANGEMENT	
WALL	1 Hop-up 2 Step ladder		
CEILING	1 Two hop-ups + scaffold board 2 Two step ladders + board		
STAIRCASE	1 Ladder, board + step ladder 2 Scaffold board + step ladder		

Fig. 66. Examples of scaffold arrangements

What safety precautions must be observed when paperhanging?

1. Make sure that step ladders are fully open.
2. Waste cuttings should not be left lying around. Put them in a waste box or bag.
3. Never leave scissors or tools on the top of steps or ledges.
4. Never leave loosened light fittings suspended by the cable.
5. When working round switches or sockets make sure that the electricity is switched off at the mains or the appropriate fuse is removed.
6. Wash hands thoroughly. Most pastes contain fungicides which can cause stomach disorders if ingested.

How are tools carried when papering?

A paperhanging apron with a wide pocket should be worn in order to keep the tools close at hand and at the same time leaving both hands free to handle the paper.

What method is used to fit a length of paper into a space narrower than the width of the paper?

Measure the space at the top, middle and bottom and use the largest measurement.

Paste the length of paper in the normal way and fold end to end.

Position the paper so that the edge is in line with the edge of the paste board.

Hold the rule with the left hand with the required length out across the paper.

Hold a pencil at the end of the rule with one hand and position the other firmly against the edge of the board and draw a line the length of the paper. Cut the paper to size along this line, trim surplus into angle after hanging.

How is the paper hung around an internal angle?

The first length should be allowed to turn round the angle about 5 mm. The second length should be hung to a plumbed

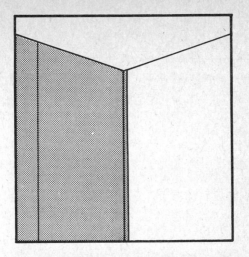

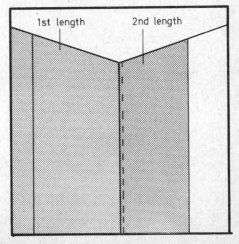

Fig. 67. Hanging wallpaper round an internal angle

line and positioned close to the angle to overlap the turn round of length one (Fig. 67).

Where a length has to be cut narrower, use the method described above making allowance for a 5 mm turn round. The remaining piece is used on the return wall to continue the match.

If the wrap round exceeds 10 mm the paper may pull away from the angle and be easily torn.

How is paper hung round an external angle?

Try to plan lengths so that the external angle falls near the middle of a length; butt joints on or near external angles tend

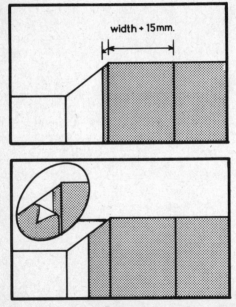

Fig. 68. Hanging wallpaper round an external angle

82

to spring open (Fig. 68). Cut the paper wide enough to lap round the angle about 15 mm. The remaining piece must be used on the return wall and positioned just short of the corner.

How is the paper hung round a window reveal?

Measure one width of paper from the window and mark the wall using a plumb line as a guide (Fig. 69). Hang length to the line, cut it level with the top of the reveal and the window sill (Fig. 70). Insert matching piece at top of reveal and wrap round paper into the reveal (Fig. 71).

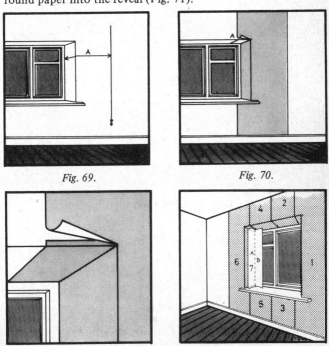

Fig. 69.

Fig. 70.

Fig. 71.

Fig. 72.

Figs 69–72. Sequence of hanging wallpaper round a window reveal

Subsequent short lengths are then hung over and under the window and the opposite side treated as before, cutting off any surplus or inserting a narrow strip depending on how the lengths work out (Fig. 72).

What methods are used to fit paper round obstructions?

Flush switches and socket-outlets. Switch off the electricity mains supply or remove the appropriate fuse. Loosen or remove switch cover. Hang paper over the switch, cut from

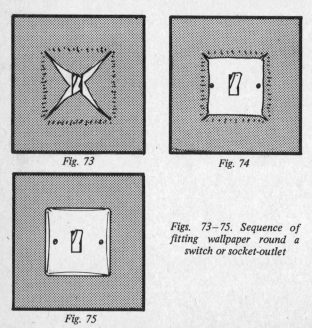

Fig. 73

Fig. 74

Figs. 73–75. Sequence of fitting wallpaper round a switch or socket-outlet

Fig. 75

the centre of the switch to corners (Fig. 73). Cut off surplus leaving hole slightly smaller than cover. Carefully tuck paper behind cover before tightening screws (Figs 74 and 75). A metallic paper must be cut to fit the light switch. If ends are tucked in they may make contact with the electric points and short.

Fig. 76. To paper around an immovable switch or fixture, a star-shaped cut should be made

Immovable fixtures. Hang paper and locate fixture making an impression with fingers. Make star cut so that the paper fits neatly round fixture (Fig. 76). The surplus is trimmed off using small scissors or sharp knife.

How are adjacent surfaces protected from paste?

If paste is allowed to dry on an adjacent surface, it may result in unsightly brown stains on emulsion paint or cause cracking and flaking of oil based paints. This can be avoided by ensuring that all surplus paste is removed immediately with a clean damp sponge.

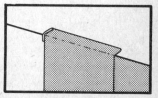

Fig. 77. A small fold on the top of the paper will prevent paste getting onto paint or the ceiling

A small fold at the top of each length will prevent paste from soaking into the paint or paper on the ceiling (Fig. 77). The length can be trimmed to size through the fold.

Will paste harm the face of the paper?

If allowed to dry, paste will leave a smear on the surface of the paper and in some cases will cause undue stress resulting in springing of the joints.

The most susceptible papers are those with metallic colours used in the design. Such papers are prone to darkening especially when the paste is starch based.

Cellulose paste is less likely to harm the surface but in any event it should be carefully removed with a clean damp sponge, used in a mopping motion rather than rubbing, which could mark some delicate papers.

How can a firm bond be ensured when it is necessary to lap vinyl paper?

The surface of vinyl paper is designed to repel normal adhesives to reduce the risk of paste marks especially on pre-pasted types. This presents a problem when vinyl has to be lapped at internal and external angles.

There are special p.v.a. lap adhesives or latex type (such a 'Copydex') which can be used for this purpose. It is most important to remove the surplus immediately with a clean damp cloth.

Is a paste-board required when using ready pasted papers?

Although the paper is not actually pasted on the board, it is desirable to have some form of working surface in order to cut and match the lengths in the normal way.

A flush door taken off its hinges provides an ideal surface if a paperhanging table is not readily available.

How is a length of ready-pasted paper hung to a wall?

Lengths are cut in the usual way. Each length should be marked on the reverse side to indicate the top. The length is then rolled from top to bottom so that the top is in the centre of the roll.

The trough is filled with approximately two-thirds cold water and placed at the base of the wall where the length is to be hung. Place the rolled length under water with the loose end (bottom) nearest to the wall. Reroll the length making sure to keep it under water, this ensures complete wetting of the paste and for average room lengths takes the required amount of wetting time. When rerolled, the top is in the correct position for drawing and offering to the wall (Fig. 78).

Fig. 78. Drawing-out ready-pasted paper from a trough

A clean sponge is used to smooth out the paper and remove excess water from the face of the paper. During hanging the bottom of the length should be allowed to trail into the trough, this allows the water to drain back into the trough and not onto the floor.

How is a length of ready-pasted paper hung to a ceiling or staircase wall where the water trough cannot be placed close to the surface?

Cut the paper to the required lengths. Place the water trough in a convenient position, such as the paperhanging table. Select the required length and prepare it by rolling, immersing and rerolling as described in previous question.

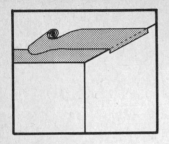

Fig. 79. Ready-pasted papers can be put up without the necessity for folding

After immersing for the appropriate time, lift out the rolled length and allow the excess water to drain off. The length can then be rolled out over the surface with ease and without the necessity for folding (Fig. 79).

Is a paperhanging brush used for ready-pasted papers?

A large decorator's sponge is used in preference to a paperhanging brush. This is capable of absorbing excess water from the surface and can be cleaned more readily.

Can wallpapers be made washable?

Yes, by the application of a clear emulsion varnish. Care must be taken to ensure that each wall is completed with a full wet coat. Lapping over dried edges will cause uneven sheen.

Some wallpapers contain water-soluble dyes which may be affected by emulsion varnish, a small test should be made first. The varnish when dry produces a non-yellowing film impervious to grease, dust, food stains, tobacco smoke and finger marks and can be washed with a mild detergent solution.

How can scissors be kept sharp?

Scissors can be kept sharp by observing the following rules.
1. Remove paste from blades after trimming each length.
2. Before storing, clean thoroughly using warm water and dry off with a cloth. Do not use abrasive materials which may damage the blades.
3. Smear with oil or grease when not in use.
4. Keep the 'set' properly adjusted by use of the pivot screw.
5. The cutting edge can be resharpened by using a metal file or special sharpening tool, care must be taken to keep the angle constant along the length of the blade.
6. Occasionally the blades will need to be hollow ground, this is done on a power driven grinding wheel and requires a certain amount of skill.

What is the cause of wallpaper blistering?

The most common cause is insufficient time to soak after pasting. Thin simplex papers can normally be hung immediately after pasting but heavy duplex embossed papers require soaking time, otherwise they continue to expand on the wall causing the paper to push off in the form of blisters.

Other causes are:
1. Condensation, cold damp walls, non-porous surfaces such as unlined oil painted walls, which cause the paste to dry too slowly.
2. Poorly adhering lining paper which absorbs water from the paste and pulls away from the substrate.
3. Paste applied unevenly which causes uneven expansion of the paper.
4. Paste mixed too thin which causes excessive wetting of the paper.

Why do some edges of wallpaper spring open?

An excessively porous or powdery surface will absorb freshly applied paste from the paper leaving it too dry to bond to the surface. The tension set up during drying causes the paper to curl at the edges. This can also be caused by weak paste because the bond is insufficient when the paper dries and tensions.

Another very common cause is paste misses along edges or thin applications which dry out quickly.

How can gaps between joints be avoided?

Uneven surfaces will make butt jointing difficult. Also over-soaking may cause undue shrinkage leaving gaps between joints.

Edges of the paper should be carefully butted together before thoroughly smoothing the paper down from the centre out towards the edges.

What can cause wallpaper to become stained?

The common causes are:
1. Moisture from a damp patch will carry salts and impurities to the surface of the paper leaving a brown stain round the edge of the patch. The source of dampness must be found and rectified and the surface allowed to dry out thoroughly before redecorating. Broken rainwater pipes, gaps round door and window frames, pointing in need of repair and blocked cavity wall are all common causes of moisture penetration.
2. Slow drying of paste in cold rooms or surface condensation will encourage mould growth and discolouration of the printing inks. Some form of heating will usually help to avoid this.
3. Unsealed steel nail heads will cause rust staining. All exposed nails or screw heads should be sealed with oil paint.
4. Starch paste allowed to contaminate the face of the paper will cause unsightly stains.
5. Ballpoint pens or indelible pencils used to mark either the wall or the paper will result in staining. Use only a black lead pencil.

Can wallpaper stretch when being hung?

Yes, all papers are pliable and are capable of being stretched when pasted. Care should be taken not to overbrush the paper which may cause creasing or flattening of an embossed design.

Stretching can sometimes be used to advantage when edges do not meet on uneven walls. Slight pressure should be applied by using the whole hand spread carefully and not just the finger tips.

Can paste cause damage to paintwork?

Yes, some pastes will cause more damage than others depending on their type. No paste should be allowed to dry on painted surfaces as this may cause flaking and staining. Even the thinnest smear of paste left on a surface can cause severe staining many months after the job is completed.

Usually full gloss paints are not affected if the paste is removed with a damp sponge while still wet, but low sheen finishes may absorb some of the paste and cause uneven patches of sheen when dry. Paper should be folded over at the ends to avoid the paste touching adjoining paintwork (see Fig. 77).

Why do some wallpapers match in one place but not in another?

There are many reasons for this defect, some of the more common ones are mentioned below.
1. Uneven porosity causes the paper to slide in one place and not another resulting in poor alignment of the pattern. Sizing the surface should reduce the possibility.
2. Uneven surfaces may encourage the paperhanger to stretch the paper in some places.
3. Uneven pasting causes paper to swell more in some areas than others.
4. Uneven soaking times particularly common on lengths of varying sizes, i.e. staircase wall, causes long lengths to swell and stretch more than shorter lengths.
5. Uneven brushing out causes paper to distort.

6. Hand-trimmed papers may have been poorly trimmed.

7. Papers do stretch and the weight of a pasted length is sufficient to pull a paper out of shape. This is common on long lengths and when embossed papers are used.

If the cause is unavoidable the pattern should be matched at eye level so that any mismatching will be less noticeable.

What causes some papers to appear a slightly different colour even though of the same pattern?

The most common cause is the minute differences between different batches of ink during the printing process. It is essential that all papers being used in one room have the same batch number marked on the label or printed on the end of the roll.

Even when the numbers are identical a careful visual check should be made before the lengths are cut.

Other causes may be:

1. Reversing alternate lengths when not recommended by the manufacturer. This may cause a change in light reflection.
2. Reflection of adjacent surfaces such as carpets, curtains or furnishings. These can cause an apparent change of colour.

4

PAINT DEFECTS

What causes paint to flake?

Poor adhesion. This may be caused by poor surface preparation or moisture in the substrate. The most common causes are:
1. Applying oil or emulsion systems to powdery or chalking existing paints.
2. Condensation entering through small splits in the film or moisture entering the surface from outside causing the paint to lose its grip of the substrate.
3. Applying paint to wet, greasy or dirty surfaces.
4. Applying incorrect paints to substrates which have excessive expansion and contraction such as unseasoned or old timber; or non-ferrous metals.

What is 'cissing' or 'cessing'?

A very glossy or greasy surface will cause the paint to be repelled by the surface which is known as cissing or cessing. All surfaces must be thoroughly cleaned and abraded before any paint is applied.

What causes paint films to crack?

1. When the top coat or coats are less flexible than the previous coatings or the substrate onto which they are applied, the underneath coat moves with sufficient force to cause the top film to split and crack.
2. If a brittle adhesive is applied over a recent paint film it contracts on drying and can cause the paint film to crack.

The most common examples are:
  (a) The advanced weathering and ageing of a paint film.
  (b) Applying paint films over thick coatings of flexible gloss varnish.
  (c) Applying paints to primers or undercoats which are soft or not fully dry.
  (d) Applying an oil or emulsion paint system over a thick bituminous coating.
  (e) Failure to remove traces of size or paste from adjoining painted surfaces when paperhanging.

How can excessive bittiness in a paint film be avoided?

There are many causes of this defect which tend to make gloss finishes appear dull and also makes cleaning of such surfaces more difficult and less effective.

The following procedures keep bittiness to a minimum.
1. Ensure that bits in existing coatings have been removed during preparation and the surface wiped free of loose particles.
2. Check that brush and paint kettles are perfectly clean.
3. Decant paint into the kettle through a metal strainer or nylon cloth to remove any bits, especially when using paints from opened cans (See Figs. 49, 50 and 51).
4. Make sure surrounding areas are swept and if possible dampen floor to avoid airborne dust. This is the most difficult aspect to control.
5. Before applying paint, wipe over the surface with a tack cloth to remove any fine surface dust.

Why are gloss paints prone to run?

Because of their comparatively low pigment content gloss paints have greater fluidity than most other coatings and, if applied unevenly, they tend to sag in the areas which are thickest (see Fig. 46). These paints also are prone to run from around surface projections such as door or window furniture and mouldings or surface imperfections such as holes or non-abraded lumps.

What happens to paint if it is overbrushed or overrolled?

All paints must be applied and laid off before the thinner has evaporated to allow the film formers to flow out into a smooth film. If the paint is brushed or rolled after the thinner has evaporated a course texture is left in the film. With many oil paints a scaley effect is left in the film when they are over-brushed.

Overbrushing thixotropic coatings tends to break down the gel qualities of the paint making it more prone to run and lessening its capacity.

How is it possible to avoid collecting paint on sill or door edges?

When the two faces which meet at the edge are coated remove as much paint from the brush as possible on the edge of the

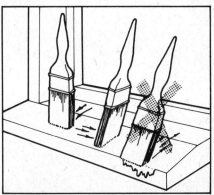

Fig. 80. To avoid excess paint collecting on edges or sills, the paint should be brushed carefully along or away from the angle

95

paint kettle and drag it carefully along the angle (Fig. 80). This should absorb or distribute the excessive paint and avoid the fat edge.

Are there climatic conditions which can cause paint to lose its gloss entirely?

Yes. Moisture such as rain, fog, frost, dew or condensation which forms on the surface of gloss paints or varnishes during their drying period can completely remove the gloss qualities of the film former. It is a severe form of the defect called 'blooming' which in milder forms appears as a milky film over the surface.

This is avoided by either protecting the surface with sheets or screens during the drying process, or by carefully controlling the time of the day when commencing painting.

In winter and autumn months, it is advisable to apply gloss finishes as early in the day as possible to avoid the evening dampness affecting the film.

What causes gloss paints to dry with an uneven sheen?

The absorption of the paint medium into the underlying surface. The most common causes are:
1. Absorbent undercoats due to being left too long before applying finish.
2. Applying gloss direct onto unpainted or only sealed absorbent surfaces.
3. Unsealed areas of filler.
4. Poorly prepared surfaces leaving rough areas which will refract light from the gloss finish.

What causes the small coloured growths on various interior surfaces?

These are mould growths which are airborne spores that are attracted by damp unventilated atmospheres and grow rapidly on surfaces which contain or are coated with organic substances. Starch paste, glue size and paints containing drying oils are ideal materials for supplying sustenance to mould growth.

These growths are very common in damp, dark, cold places such as cellars or neglected buildings. They can grow in warm rooms where ventilation is poor, such as behind curtains, in cupboards and at low levels.

Mould growths can commonly be found on the bottom putties of north facing windows where the cold aspect causes condensation. Once established in a building the spores quickly multiply and spread rapidly.

How is mould growth treated?

All affected wallpaper must be completely stripped and burnt. If mould is deep seated in a paint system this also must be removed completely. Mildew forms growing on the surface can be removed only by washing with a solution of four parts water and one part household bleach. This both kills and removes the growth from the surface.

Very severe cases will require treatment with a mould inhibitor which can be obtained from most paint manufacturers. The manufacturer's instructions should be followed carefully.

When redecorating, all pastes and sizes must contain a fungicide. Paints containing fungicide can be obtained but these are necessary in only the most severe cases.

Improving the heating or ventilation in a room which has been affected is the most reliable method of preventing mould growth re-occurring.

What is the cause of smoky or dirty stains on walls and ceilings?

These stains are caused by the heated air from around the radiator rising and carrying airborne dirt and dust with it which settles on the colder parts of the walls (Fig. 81).

In the case of ceilings the heat is conducted through the ceiling between the joists leaving the dirt deposits on the ceiling (see Fig. 83a). This is known as pattern staining.

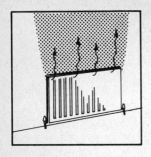

Fig. 81. Hot air from radiators can discolour paintwork or paper

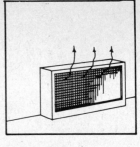

Fig. 82. Encasing the heater (or radiator) or fitting shelving will help to prevent discolouring

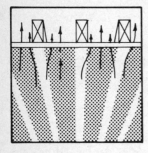

Fig. 83a. Heat conducted through the joints can leave dirt deposits on the ceiling

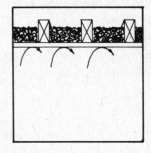

Fig. 83b. Insulating the ceiling between the joists with glass fibre or similar material

Can painting effectively cure pattern staining?

No. Insulating the ceiling between the joists with glass fibre or similar material or preventing the convection currents touching the walls by casing in or shelving over the radiators are the most likely ways of curing pattern staining (Fig. 82). The use of gloss paints will enable the dirt deposits to be readily removed.

The application of highly textured materials such as plastic paint or textured wall coverings may visually mask the stain. Also, covering the ceiling with insulating tiles or sheeting will help to reduce the effect of pattern staining.

Will paint prevent the spread of dry or wet rot of wood?

No. If dry or wet rot is present in timber it will need to be eradicated.

Painting can help prevent the initial attack taking place by protecting the timber from moisture penetration. This is especially the case when joinery is fixed to adjoining surfaces containing moisture such as brickwork. All door and window frames should be well primed on all faces before they are fixed into their openings. Fascia boards and timber cladding fixed externally should be treated in a similar manner.

Paint also forms a very effective barrier where moisture will lay and slowly soak into timber, such as door and window sills. The application of an extra coat of finishing paint in these situations can help to prevent deterioration of timber surfaces.

What may cause paint to dry very slowly?

There may be many causes, but the most common are as follows.
1. *Poor preparation*. Failure to remove completely greasy or wax deposits, especially on skirtings and surfaces which are constantly handled, i.e. doors, newel posts and handrails. Failing to remove all traces of washing soda or sugar soap may also retard the paints drying.
2. *Lack of oxygen*. As most paints are air drying, inadequate ventilation will slow the drying speed. Moist atmospheres and cold draughts will have a similar effect.
3. *Temperature*. Very low temperatures will slow the evaporation of the thinners in the applied film and the whole process

will be retarded. This is particularly noticeable on the interior face of external walls.

4. *Admixing*. If large amounts of stainers are added to paint to change the colour they can cause an inbalance in the formulation and slow the drying process. An excess of universal stainers can prevent the paint drying at all. Adding linseed oil to paint considerably slows its setting. Also use of the wrong thinners, i.e. paraffin or petrol may slow the drying.

5. *Bitumen*. Surfaces coated with bituminous coatings or creosote will considerably slow the setting of spirit-borne paints. Unless properly sealed, these coatings may prevent any paints achieving maximum hardness.

Will paint prevent corrosion?

Yes. providing no rust is on the surface when painting commences.

The primary function of paint coatings on metal is to form a barrier against the elements that promote corrosion, moisture and oxygen. For a paint system to be effective it must form an unbroken film over the whole surface, be sufficiently thick at least 125 microns (usually five coats of paint), and adhere well to the surface. The first coat must also be a rust inhibitive primer.

To make the paint adhere well, the metal should be free from all traces of rust, millscale and grease. Many methods of preparation are available which vary greatly in effectiveness and cost.

What can cause paint to change colour?

There are three common forms of colour change:
1. Yellowing of white paints.
2. The affect on some coloured pigments by light or chemical action, and
3. Bleeding of old paint coatings.

Yellowing is the result of the slow effect of the paints film former changing colour; it is most noticeable in white paints.

This occurs most rapidly in the absence of light, therefore window walls, areas behind pictures or furniture, dark cupboards and door edges are the places it will be most noticeable.

A few pigments are prone to fade or lose some of their colour when exposed to strong sunlight, these include certain greens and oranges. Lime in plaster, brickwork or asbestos cement can, when wet, destroy certain coloured pigments in paint and wallpaper. Colour change may occur in new houses while the walls are still wet, or in old houses when moisture has penetrated severely from outside.

Some red and orange paints are very difficult to repaint with another colour because the pigments are dissolved by the new coating and stain the paint. This defect is known as bleeding. It is most likely to happen when using spirit borne paints. Creosote and bituminous coatings will also bleed through spirit borne paints applied directly to them. Bleeding can be prevented by first applying a barrier coat. These coatings are based on emulsion, leafing aluminium or shellac.

Why does varnish have less durability on outside surfaces?

Because varnish does not have a pigment content the medium is more vulnerable to attack by the ultra violet (uv) action in sunlight which prematurely makes the film brittle.

This brittleness is a disadvantage externally as the majority of varnished surfaces are timber which will expand and contract with the changes in temperature leading to early breakdown of the coating. For this reason, it is necessary for varnished surfaces to be recoated more often than surfaces painted with pigmented coatings.

What happens if oil paint is applied over bitumen or creosote?

Materials which have bitumen or coal-tar bases are soluble in white spirit which is the thinner used in oil paints; the dissolved bitumen will mix with the newly applied coating and discolour it. These materials may also slow or prevent drying of the new paint. This can be overcome by sealing the bitumen coating, before applying the oil paint, with coatings not containing white spirit. Many paint manufacturers supply such barrier coatings.

Bitumen, being thermoplastic, will soften if heated causing the harder coatings applied to them to crack. Where possible it is more practical to re-coat with similar materials.

In what way does old paint deteriorate when stored in a closed tin?

Most paints can be kept for several years without serious deterioration apart from a skin forming on the surface. The main problem is pigment settlement as the solid part of the paint slowly sinks to the bottom of the tin. This can usually be mixed again by thorough stirring.

Some paints may also thicken on storage. If the paint can be stirred but is too thick to apply, then a little thinner will usually restore the paint to a workable consistency. If the consistency resembles a sticky jelly which cannot be stirred easily, then the resin has started to solidify and the paint cannot be used.

What causes paint film breakdown on bottom window rails and cills?

Moisture and the movement of timber. There are several contributory factors:

1. Sills should be sealed on all sides before fixing to prevent moisture penetration from behind.
2. The end grain of timber is particularly porous so the ends of cills must receive special attention to ensure they are adequately sealed.
3. Defective putties allow rain and condensation to run down and soak into the timber.
4. Movement at the joints between the stiles and bottom rails can allow moisture to penetrate behind the paint film. These areas are usually very exposed to the elements and are worthy of special attention including an extra coat of gloss finish on the sills.

5

SCAFFOLDING

When are stepladders used?

Stepladders are the most popular and commonly used form of access scaffold for internal work where a firm level base is more readily available. They can be used independently or in conjunction with a scaffold board in pairs to form a working platform. Steps may feel insecure if the working platform is higher than 2 m.

Sizes range from 5-10 treads high and are constructed of either timber or aluminium.

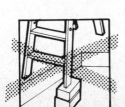

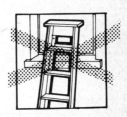

Fig. 84. Unsafe methods of using steps

What precautions are necessary to ensure safety when using stepladders?

Safety checks

Do not use steps with either:
    loose or slack hinges,
    frayed or uneven ropes,
    missing or loose treads.
Make sure steps are fully open when in use.
Do no use steps as a ladder in a closed position.
Do not place scaffold boards on top of steps, use ladder steps.
Always dismantle scaffold before moving.

How should a ladder be made secure when in use?

Ladders should be secured at the top to prevent movement across the work face, and also at the bottom or in the middle to prevent the base slipping.

Methods of achieving this will vary depending on the surroundings and the nature of the building. All tying of ladders should be made around the stiles and not to the rungs (Fig. 85).

Fig. 85. Ladders should be tied by the stiles and not around the rungs

Top fixing. Always tie ladders to something substantial (roof rafters or firmly fixed screw eyes into the brick or barge board, and never to gutters or rainwater pipes.
Bottom fixing. There are several different methods depending on the type of ground on which the ladder has to stand:
    (a) Anchor by guy ropes from stiles into ground or wall supports (Fig. 86).

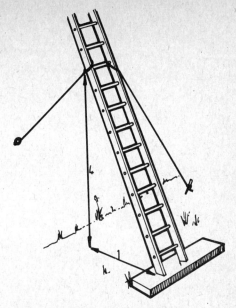

Fig. 86. Guy ropes from the stiles can be
used to secure ladders

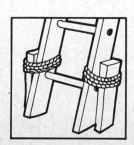

Fig. 87. The ladder can be tied to
wedges driven into the ground

105

(b) Tied to wedges driven into ground at base of ladder (Fig. 87).

(c) Lay sand bags or similar weights at base of ladder (Fig. 88).

(d) If none of these are available or practical it will be necessary to have a person standing on the bottom rung (footing) for the duration of the work (Fig. 89).

Fig. 88. Sandbags can be placed at the bottom of the ladder

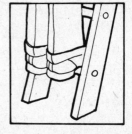

Fig. 89. Standing on the bottom of the ladder will keep it secure

Various forms of patent ladder feet are also available to help prevent the ladder slipping.

When working on a ladder its angle and placement is very important. A simple rule for this is for every four vertical metres the ladder rises the base should extent 1 m from the workface so forming an angle of 75° (Fig. 86). If it is closer to the wall it can tip back; further away it is likely to slide.

106

Fig. 90. Typical use of ladder scaffold board and stepladder

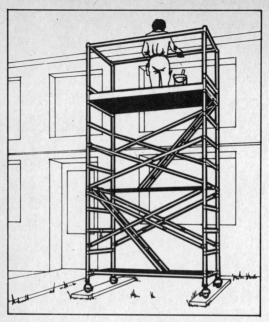

Fig. 91. Using a mobile tower. The wheels must be locked and, if used on soft ground, the weight should be spread to prevent sinking

Fig. 92. The stiles at the top of the ladder should be bound to prevent damage to walls

When are scaffold boards used and in what conditions are they safe?

Scaffold boards or planks are used to form working platforms on various forms of tubular scaffold and in conjunction with both stepladders and trestles (Fig. 90).

The timbers should be softwood and be straight-grained and free from knots and splits.

Boards rarely exceed 4 m in length. Widths vary according to the thickness: 50 mm thick boards are usually 200 mm wide and boards exceeding 50 mm may be 150 mm wide.

Safety. When used as a working platform the gaps between the boards should not exceed 25 mm. Boards should never over-hang supports by more than four times their thickness. Twisted, split or rotten boards should never be used.

What is a unit scaffold?

Unit scaffolds are very adaptable systems of prefabricated units usually made from galvanised steel or aluminium. The units can be locked together without the need for loose fittings to form safe access towers and working platforms without the need for specialist knowledge of scaffolding (Fig. 91).

They are designed to be safe provided that the erection instructions are followed exactly. To avoid the risk of towers tipping, the height should not exceed the narrowest width more than 3 times.

How should ladders be prevented from damaging walls?

The most simple method is to bind the top of the stiles with sacking or similar material (Fig. 92). When soiled these can be changed.

What is lightweight staging?

A reinforced 500 mm wide slatted platform which can span up to 7.2 m without intermediate support (Fig. 93). Due to their

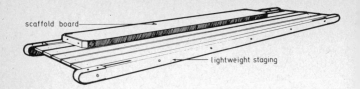

Fig. 93. The difference between a scaffold board and a lightweight staging

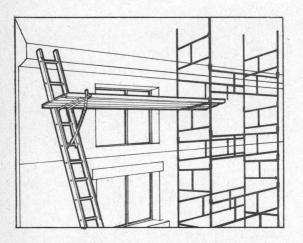

Fig. 94. Lightweight staging used in conjunction with a ladder bracket and prefabricated tower

greater width these platforms are not suitable for use with stepladders but are ideally suitable for use with trestles, ladder brackets and towers (Fig. 94). They are designed to bear the weight of three men.

110

6

WORK PROCEDURE

What is the correct order of operations when painting the outside of a house?

As with most painting work the furthest or highest point should be started first (Fig. 95). Each section of work should be prepared before painting is started, including repairs to

Fig. 95. Correct order of operations when painting the outside of a house

guttering, reglazing and any defective rendering. This will avoid debris, dust etc. falling onto newly completed work.

It is generally more practical to prepare, and then paint, each elevation separately so preventing prepared surfaces being left exposed to the elements for any length of time.

Fences, gates and small outbuildings should be left until last as the latter often provide ideal storage for plant and materials during the work.

How is reglazing carried out?

Reglazing is carried out during the initial preparation so as to allow time for the new putties to harden before they are repainted. The procedure is:
1. Remove broken glass.
2. Hack out old putties and remove glazing sprigs.
3. Prime rebates to prevent shrinkage of new putties.
4. Apply bedding putties and push new glass into position.
5. Hold the glass in place with glazing sprigs (small pins) or clips when reglazing metal sashes (Fig. 96).

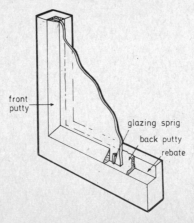

Fig. 96. Reglazing a window

112

6. Apply front putties. A special metal putty is available for metal sashes which is more suitable than traditional linseed oil putty used for timber.

Is it necessary to paint the inside of gutters?

This will depend on the material used for their construction. Plastic gutters require no painting but it is necessary to clean them to prevent blockages.

Zinc, mild steel and cast iron must be painted after cleaning, scraping and brushing out. Bituminous paint is ideal for this purpose. Asbestos and concrete gutters do not require painting to protect them, but moss and lichen are likely to grow on them and may cause blockages; painting will help to prevent this.

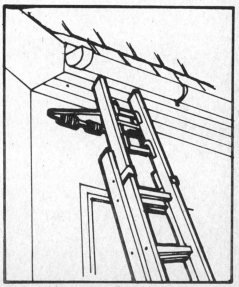

Fig. 97. Use of ladder steps

113

What methods can be used to give safe access to gutters and upstairs windows?

Ladders generally provide the simplest form of access to work at heights, provided the correct safety precautions are met. It is rarely safe or practical to rest ladders against gutters and if the ladder is rested on the wall beneath them, the eaves overhang presents a problem when the gutters require to be prepared and painted.

Ladder stays can help to overcome this problem as they support the ladder away from the surface giving greater freedom of movement (Fig. 97). For more extensive work a ladder bracket scaffold or prefabricated tower could be used.

How are lawns and plants protected when painting or moving scaffolds?

To prevent ladders sinking into flower beds or lawns the weight should be spread by supporting the base of the ladder on a scaffold board (Fig. 98).

Fig. 98. To prevent ladders sinking into soft earth a scaffold board can be used to spread the weight

Flower beds and shrubs will look unsightly if flakes or splashes of paint are allowed to fall on them. This can be avoided by tying back shrubs and covering them with lightweight sheeting.

Vines and wall climbing plants present a greater problem especially if the surface has to be painted. Where possible the plant should be released from the wall and supported (to prevent breaking) on a pair of trestles or steps until the work is completed.

If several rooms in a house are being decorated at what stage is the staircase decorated?

Because the majority of rooms in a house lead from the staircase, any decorations to this area should be left until last. The movement of scaffold and furniture from room to room is likely to cause damage or mark the surfaces.

A secondary reason for leaving this work until last is that as most staircases form a link between the rooms, decoration should if possible compliment or blend with the decoration of the rooms. This decision is easier to make with the rooms completed.

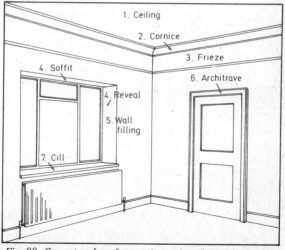

Fig. 99. Correct order of operations when decorating a room

What is the order of working when redecorating a room?

As with external work it is normal to commence work at the highest point (ceiling) working downwards towards the floor for all the various activities. The order of working is as follows:

1. Move all furniture to the centre of the room and cover the floor and furniture with dust sheets.
2. Remove all door and window furniture.
3. Prepare all surfaces including hanging of preparatory papers (lining, ingrain) to ceiling and walls if required.
4. Remove all debris, shake out dustsheets and recover floors and furniture. This will prevent any dust spoiling the finished work.
5. The painting should follow the order shown in Fig. 99 unless wallpaper is to be hung and this would be carried out after the painting is complete.

Is there any special procedure when painting a panelled door?

Yes. The following sequence is designed to avoid too many 'wet edges' which will cause thick ridges of paint. Also it enables longer strokes of the brush to be achieved on the final strokes (laying off). The order of painting (see Fig. 100) should be as follows. The arrows indicate the direction of 'laying off'.

1. Moulding.
2. Panel.
3. Top muntin.
4. Bottom muntin.
5. Top rail.
6. Lock or middle rail.
7. Bottom rail.
8. Back edge or front edge if door opens inwards.
9. Stile.
10. Stile.

How are double-hung sliding sash windows painted?

The painting of all sashes are designed so that when open or closed all facing surfaces will present a uniform colour. Fig. 101 shows the order of painting the sash from the inside.

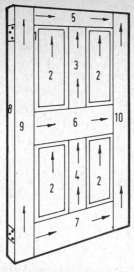

Fig. 100. Order of painting
for a panelled door

Should door and window furniture be removed before painting?

Yes. Where possible.

1. Old paint coatings on fittings may be removed without damage to surfaces.
2. The preparation and painting process will be shortened and improved in quality by not having to cut around the fittings.

   Between coats the fittings should be loosely refitted to avoid loss and in the case of doors allow them to be opened and closed.

What colour should door and casement edges be painted?

The colour is determined by what edges show when the sash or door is opened. As a general rule the back (hinge) edge will be painted when opening outwards and the front (lock) edge when opening inwards.

With casement sashes both bottom and top edges should be included with the painting of the exterior (Fig. 102).

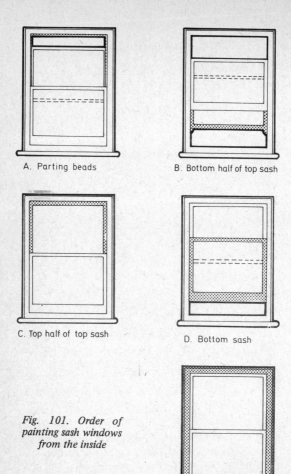

A. Parting beads

B. Bottom half of top sash

C. Top half of top sash

D. Bottom sash

Fig. 101. Order of painting sash windows from the inside

E. Architrave and cill

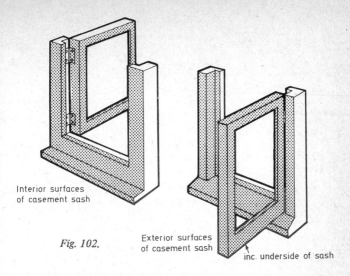

Interior surfaces
of casement sash

Fig. 102.

Exterior surfaces
of casement sash

inc. underside of sash

Is it necessary to turn off electricity before starting decorations?

This is only necessary if fittings have to be removed and wires are exposed, or if large amounts of water will be involved in the work.

The greatest problem lies where metal foils and papers are being hung, if the paper is tucked behind switch plates or power points, contact with the wires may cause a short circuit or make the material 'live'.

How can furniture and fittings be protected?

Furniture which cannot be removed should be stacked where it does not have to be constantly moved to allow easy movement of persons and scaffold to every surface to be decorated. The centre of the room is often the most convenient point.

The furniture should be completely covered with sheets with the ends either tucked in or tied to prevent movement.

Fittings that cannot be removed should be covered with paper held in position with masking tape.

119

The following types of sheets are available:

Type	Characteristics
Cotton drill dust sheets	Tough and long lasting. Washable. Absorbent, although if considerable water is being used they should be used in combination with plastic sheets.
Plastic sheets (500 or 1000 gauge only)	Waterproof. Slippery, particularly when wet. It is safer to use a cotton sheet over the plastic when wet processes are being used. Brittle when very cold. Limited life. Cheap
Paper sheets	Disposable. Very absorbent with high wet strength. Light. Convenient
Tarpaulins (heavy reinforced plastic or proofed heavy cotton)	Extremely tough. Water and chemical proof. Heavy. Expensive. Suitable when covering machinery or very large areas

How are fitted carpets protected when redecorating?

The only certain method is to have the carpets professionally lifted before work starts and relaid on completion. If this is not possible the success of all other methods is dependent upon careful working at all times and no accidents occuring.

One method is to cover the entire floor with 1000 gauge plastic. The edge of the plastic must be tightly fitted into the angle between carpet and skirting and pinned in position. If the pins or fine nails are driven through thin strips or battens of wood laid on the plastic edge a better seal is made and there is less chance of the plastic tearing.

INDEX